'You're not my type, anyway.'

Flynn's eyes ran over her slender form and she suffered agonies beneath his scrutiny. 'Too thin,' he continued harshly. 'When I hold a woman in my arms I want to feel a woman's body, a woman's curves, soft and desirable.'

Kaylie shuddered, lashed by the contempt in his scathing words, but managed with difficulty to stand her ground.

'If you'll be good enough to point out the linen cupboard I'd like to unpack and settle in.'

Dear Reader

As spring moves into summer, you can't help but think about summer holidays, and to put you in the right frame of mind this month's selection is jam-packed with exotic holiday destinations. As a tempter, why not try Patricia Wilson's new Euromance, DARK SUNLIGHT, set in sultry Spain? *And*, who knows, you may well find yourself one day visiting the very places mentioned in the novel! One thing's for sure, you're bound to have lots of fun on the way...

The Editor

When **Rachel Elliot** was a child in Aberdeen, she was frequently to be found comfortably perched in the branches of an apple tree, scribbling stories. Now she lives in the beautiful Borders, and she's still scribbling—but now from an office overlooking the stable yard of her small pony-trekking centre. She's crazy about animals, as you'd see from her motley collection of four-legged and feathered friends. Oh, yes—she also works as a reporter/presenter with Border Television. Life certainly isn't boring!

UNWANTED LEGACY

BY

RACHEL ELLIOT

MILLS & BOON LIMITED
ETON HOUSE,   18-24 PARADISE ROAD
RICHMOND,   SURREY   TW9 1SR

First published in Great Britain 1993
by Mills & Boon Limited

© Rachel Elliot 1993

Australian copyright 1993
Philippine copyright 1993
This edition 1993

ISBN 0 263 78035 X

Set in Times Roman 11½ on 12 pt.
01-9306-47086 C

Made and printed in Great Britain

CHAPTER ONE

KAYLIE'S high-heeled shoes clicked a furious tattoo as she ran along the crowded pavement, dodging pedestrians in her headlong rush, almost colliding with one bemused old gentleman, her words of apology lost in the air as she hurried on past. Why did the taxi have to get stuck in a traffic jam today of all days? she thought wildly, scanning the street ahead for a zebra crossing. She'd had everything organised so perfectly, even down to investing in a smart little suit since nothing in her wardrobe had been even remotely suitable for this occasion.

Uttering up a quick prayer, she darted into the road, diving between cars and ignoring the indignant blaring of horns in her wake. Flustered as she was, she couldn't help but smile impishly at the thought of the clothes she'd gazed at so helplessly the previous day—just what the solicitor would have thought if she'd turned up in her usual favourite garb of jeans and sweat-shirt or comfortable tracksuit and trainers didn't bear thinking about.

Pausing for a second to catch her breath, she gave a hollow groan. Who was she trying to kid? She hadn't blown a hole in her savings to impress a solicitor, no matter how stuffy he should turn out to be. She'd done it purely because she needed the armour of a smart, sophisticated, totally un-Kaylie-like image. Because of Flynn.

She caught sight of her reflection in a shop window and rolled her eyes heavenward in despair. Her neat little silk blouse had come adrift from its moorings, its stand-up collar was flopping on one side, and, worst of all, after labouring for hours to coerce her unruly dark red hair into submission, the sleek French plait she'd created was coming apart at the seams, with riotous curls tumbling about her flushed cheeks in happy abandon. So much for smart and sophisticated—and it was getting later by the second.

'Oh, Kaylie,' she muttered despairingly beneath her breath. 'Wouldn't Emma just throw up her hands if she could see you now?'

She was faced with a dilemma—to risk the solicitor's wrath by turning up later still, or suffer Flynn's ridicule by turning up looking like this. She owed it to Emma to be on time—but her pride wouldn't allow her to meet Flynn in anything less than bandbox perfection.

Giving in to pride, she ducked into a convenient restaurant and made use of the ladies' cloakroom to repair the worst of the damage. After a few moments she took a deep, steadying breath and glanced in the full-length mirror, attempting to assess her own reflection objectively. Before her stood a slender, not very tall young woman, neatly attired in an elegant grey suit and navy blouse, her auburn hair pulled severely back from her heart-shaped face in a plait.

Leaning closer, she peered into the glass, relieved to see her make-up had survived the morning's traumas relatively intact, for beneath the skilfully applied cosmetics she knew perfectly well that she was as pale as a wraith. To a stranger she'd appear calm, competent and perfectly in control, which was exactly what she'd been striving for. But what about Flynn—would he be fooled so easily? Or would he look at her and see the freckle-faced tomboy who'd tagged along behind him with her heart shining in her enormous grey eyes?

She shivered, all but overwhelmed by the knowledge that she was soon to see him again, the boy who'd once put the sun and stars in the sky for her, only to disappear from her life, leaving her to sob her heartbreak into Emma's comforting arms. What sort of effect would he have on her now?

'For the love of Mike, Kaylie, you're twenty-six, not sixteen,' she admonished herself, none too gently. 'You're getting into a state because you've built him up in your mind into something closely resembling a demigod. Well, he was never that—and he's probably fat and balding now with a wife and a parcel of kids.'

The thought made her chuckle, giving her the strength to pull back her shoulders and march resolutely out of the restaurant, ignoring the waiter's puzzled stare.

Nervousness returned in a rush as she entered the solicitor's office and announced herself to the receptionist, her voice sounding distinctly shaky even to her own ears. It took a real effort, but she managed to tilt her chin up defiantly as she followed the woman into the inner sanctum, keeping her eyes forward as if her very life depended on it.

'Mr Johnstone.' Her normally graceful body had grown strangely awkward, as though it didn't even belong to her, and it took everything she had to move across the expanse of carpet to his desk without falling over her own feet. She hadn't turned her head to look, but she knew Flynn was in the room, knew it with an inner certainty that sent a strange shiver down her spine. 'I'm so terribly sorry I'm late.' She extended a languid hand to the grey-haired man behind the desk as he rose courteously to greet her. 'The traffic at this time of day is simply atrocious, I'm afraid.'

A fleeting hint of amusement glinted in the man's pale, fish-like eyes. 'Please don't give it a second's thought,' he returned graciously. 'I'm sure Mr Donovan didn't mind waiting a few minutes.'

This was it. This was the moment she'd been longing for and dreading with equal intensity— the moment when she'd have to turn and look into the vivid blue eyes she'd never been able to forget. Even as she began to swivel slowly round, harsh words cut through the air like a knife.

'I most certainly do mind. I don't have time to waste—unlike Kaylie, it would seem.'

Her smile of greeting froze as she finally found herself face to face with the man who'd been haunting her dreams for so many years. Her first conscious thought was to marvel at the changes those years had brought to him—all to his benefit, it would seem, judging by the width of his shoulders and the strong set of his jaw. So much for her crazy hopes that he'd be fat and balding—the man now rising to his feet and towering over her, as he'd always done, was a sleek, magnificent animal in human form.

Tall and powerfully built, he had hair as thick and glossy black as a raven's wing, and his eyes were intensely, hypnotisingly blue. As a teenager he'd been almost ridiculously good-looking—as a mature man, he was spellbinding. And yet... and yet there was something in those devastating looks that had never been there before—something that both repelled and fascinated her at the same time. Almost unconsciously she studied his dark, saturnine features, searching for clues in the jawline apparently carved from stone, the sensual yet forbidding mouth. She found none.

'Kaylie?' Even though he'd left his native Ireland as a teenager, he'd never lost his accent, and even though there was more than a hint of impatience in his tone now his voice was still deep, still held the soft, caressing lilt that had never failed to thrill her.

'Kaylie!'

She started out of her reverie, horrified to discover she'd been staring at him.

'Let's get this charade over, for heaven's sake,' he barked harshly. 'I've got more important matters to deal with this afternoon.'

Numbly she nodded. 'More important matters', he'd said, and the three words cut like a whiplash. For the past two weeks, ever since the solicitor's letter had arrived, she'd been on tenterhooks, certain from the start that Flynn must also be there on the appointed day for the reading of Emma's will, for, after all, if Emma had anything to bequeath to anyone it would surely be given to those she'd loved most in the world—Kaylie and Flynn. To realise this reunion after so many years apart meant so little to him was like a physical pain in her chest, and she moved like a sleep-walker to the chair he indicated, swallowing hard on the lump rising in her throat.

Emma had always said she was too easily moved to emotion, she recalled now with a bleak little smile, had always said she wore her heart on her sleeve for the whole uncaring world to see. Well, surely this would finally make her learn her lesson, for no sane person could go on carrying a torch in the face of such utter cold indifference.

'Please begin, Mr Johnstone,' she said, her voice tightly controlled, betraying nothing of what she was really feeling. 'I don't wish to take up any more of Mr Donovan's valuable time than I can possibly help.'

The solicitor nodded gravely. 'Very well. As I'm sure you're both aware, I asked you here today for the purpose——'

'For the purpose of reading Emma's will,' Flynn cut in testily. 'Obviously we're aware of that, man. Get on with it!'

Kaylie gripped her hands tightly together in her lap. Dammit, how could he do this? Hadn't he loved Emma too?

'Mr Donovan,' the other man remonstrated gently, 'I appreciate you don't wish to linger here any longer than is strictly necessary, but out of respect for the late Mrs Anderson I would ask you to curb your impatience.'

Kaylie smothered a grin. It had been a low blow, but it had worked—she could tell the dart had struck home by the dark anger in Flynn's eyes.

'Now, then.' Clearing his throat, Mr Johnstone drew a sheaf of papers on to the blotter before him. 'I shall, with no further ado, begin. The last will and testament of Mrs Emma Anderson begins, of course, with the usual legal preamble.' Obviously anticipating a protest from Flynn, he shot the younger man a mildly challenging look. 'I do not propose to skip over this section. I am not a man, Mr Donovan, Miss Alexander, who approves of short cuts.'

Kaylie heard Flynn's irritated sigh and smiled again. Emma had always told him he was in too much of a hurry.

'The world won't topple off its axis just because you've stopped to smell the flowers for a little while, my lad.' The voice which had scolded, encouraged, teased and loved them both for so many years floated back to her now, and for a second the feeling of loss was so intense that Kaylie was forced to close her eyes, bracing herself against the piercing sorrow that had grown no less over the weeks since Emma's death.

'Miss Alexander, are you all right?'

She looked up into pale, concerned eyes and gave a reassuring smile. 'I'm fine, thank you.'

He nodded. 'Very well. Then I'll proceed.'

He began to read, his voice sonorous and solemn, and she focused all her attention on him, desperately trying to keep her mind free of thoughts of the man sitting just a few inches away, close enough that she could have reached out to touch him. Once she would have done just that, without giving it a second thought. Once they'd shared an easy, laughing companionship. In those uncomplicated days she could hug Flynn with the same unthinking affection she had shown Emma. The very notion of touching this remote, angry man now was patently ludicrous and she felt a pang of loss for that other relationship. The Flynn Donovan she'd once known had apparently disappeared forever, to be replaced by this cold-eyed stranger.

It had all been very different on their first meeting, when she'd been a confused and bewildered twelve-year-old, devastated by the loss of her parents and brother in a train crash. Emma, her father's cousin and the only living relative she possessed, had instantly come forward to offer Kaylie a home in her big old rambling farmhouse in rural Perthshire, a very different environment from the busy Edinburgh streets where Kaylie had grown up.

There had been little contact between Kaylie's father and Emma over the years, and for the tearful girl it was like being handed over to a complete stranger. But, though she'd never had children of her own, Emma had understood her anxiety, shouldering her through the anguish of this huge change in her life.

Learning of Flynn's existence had been another shock, for she hadn't known about the young Irish boy Emma had taken under her wing on his arrival in Scotland, friendless and practically penniless, but with a burning ambition to make a success of his life.

'He's a fine young man,' Emma told her as they travelled by train towards Perthshire. 'I'm sure you two will get along just fine together.'

'But why does he live with you?' Kaylie queried, faintly jealous. After just a couple of days in Emma's warm and loving company, she was unwilling to share the woman with anyone else. 'He's not a relation.'

Emma shrugged her broad shoulders. 'No, he's not, but that doesn't make my home any the less his.' She glanced at the young girl by her side, her brown eyes warm. 'Flynn's a typical Irishman—mad keen on horses. As soon as he was old enough he started writing letters to everyone he could think of who had any kind of interest in the horse world and who might be able to give him a job. One of the letters came to my friend Joe McBlain, who runs a training yard not far from where I live. Joe liked the sound of Flynn and offered him work, and I agreed to give him bed and board.'

'But you didn't even know him,' Kaylie remonstrated. 'Or anything about him.'

'What was there to know?' Affection mingled with amusement in Emma's broad smile. 'Only that the lad needed somewhere to stay, and there was I, rattling round in a big old farmhouse all by myself.'

'You won't be rattling round now,' Kaylie said. 'You'll have two of us.'

'And I'll be a very happy woman.' Emma put her arm round Kaylie's narrow shoulders and gave her a squeeze. 'I never thought I'd have a family of my own, but now I do.'

He was waiting for them at the station—a tall, slender sixteen-year-old. Tears came to her eyes when she saw him, for he was about the same age and build as the brother she'd lost. But there the resemblance ended. Michael had had sandy-coloured hair and hazel eyes and he'd worn a permanent cheeky grin. Flynn's hair was jet-black, his vivid blue eyes a startling contrast. When he saw Kaylie he smiled and a lock of his carefully combed hair fell into his eyes. She lost her heart to him in the space of that wordless exchange and for the first time in her life became speechless with shyness. He exchanged an under-standing glance with Emma and swung her heavy suitcase easily off the ground.

'Now then, little lass,' he said in his soft brogue, 'let's be getting you home. You look as if you need a good hot meal and a long sleep.'

Still unable to find words, she followed him to the station forecourt, where he had a taxi waiting, watching silently as he helped the driver stow the luggage in the boot. Then he turned and gave her a friendly wink and she blushed scarlet.

Emma chuckled. 'Don't you go falling for that Irish charm now, Kaylie,' she teased. 'This young devil already has all the girls for miles around swooning at his feet.'

Flynn grinned broadly and put his arm round Emma's shoulders. 'You know I only have eyes for you, me old darlin'!'

She gave him a friendly shove. 'I'll give you old, you cheeky young varmint!'

They kept up the teasing flow of banter all the way back to the farmhouse, and Kaylie gradually began to relax. He was so unlike any other sixteen-year-old boy she'd ever met—Michael's friends had been fun, but they'd all been obsessed by football and motorbikes. To them she'd simply been the little sister of a mate, who was tolerated and occasionally allowed to tag along. Flynn seemed much more mature. She said as much to Emma later that day as they unpacked Kaylie's cases.

Emma paused in the middle of filling a drawer. 'Flynn hasn't had an easy life,' she said carefully. 'He's one of ten children, but his family weren't very well off.'

'You mean they were poor?' Kaylie's grey eyes opened wide in sympathy.

Emma shook her head. 'Not the way Flynn tells it.' She smiled softly. 'That boy has the ability to look behind and beyond material possessions. He knows true riches lie in things other than money. And he has a big heart. He can never resist waifs and strays—I've had more abandoned pets and birds with broken wings brought home to me since he's been here than I ever knew existed.'

'Then he's like you,' Kaylie said quietly.

'What do you mean?' Emma slid her a questioning look.

'Just that you take in waifs and strays too—
like me and Flynn.'

For answer Emma took Kaylie in her arms and
hugged her. 'You're neither waif nor stray, my
love,' she said fiercely. 'Nor is Flynn. You're
simply two young creatures dealt a raw hand by
fate.' Tenderly she stroked a lock of hair back
from Kaylie's face. 'We three are going to get on
just fine together, you mark my words.'

Dragging her thoughts back to the present,
Kaylie's eyes narrowed as she gave Flynn an assessing look. Where had he gone, the boy who'd
nursed birds with broken wings? There was little
sign of him in this hard-eyed, distant man. What
had happened in the years since she'd last seen
him? He'd disappeared on her sixteenth birthday,
just upped and left without a word of explanation then or since. Even now, ten years on, she
could still feel the anguish she'd suffered on that
day, discovering that he'd gone. She'd tried so
many, many times to make Emma tell her where
he'd gone, or even just why he'd gone, but though
the older woman was sympathetic she'd never be
drawn, saying simply that Flynn had to make his
own way in life.

As ludicrous as it seemed now, her ridiculous
heart had turned somersaults at the thought of
seeing him again. Well, if nothing else, perhaps
this encounter would at last help her to lay the
ghost, she thought bleakly. For far too long she'd
carried the memory of vivid blue Irish eyes, and
it didn't take a psychiatrist to work out why she'd
never been able to give her heart to anyone else.

Heaven knew, she'd tried often enough—even though she wasn't exactly beautiful, her lively personality and dancing eyes had attracted a more than impressive number of interested men. But in the end something had always held her back from making a real commitment, and now, perhaps for the first time, she understood just what that something had been. She'd unconsciously measured every man beside her memory of Flynn—and found them all wanting.

The realisation almost made her laugh out loud. How could she have been such a fool? She'd spent years carrying a torch for someone who no longer existed—it took just one glance at that stubborn jaw and those unfeeling eyes to know that the Flynn she remembered was long gone. If he'd ever been there in the first place. But even as the cynical thought entered her mind she rejected it. Flynn Donovan the man might be a very different animal from the tender-hearted young lad she'd known, but she hadn't been mistaken all those years ago—she couldn't have been. Something had happened since they'd been apart—something which had turned him from friend to stranger—and perhaps she'd never know just what that was.

Maybe it was better that she didn't know, she told herself resolutely, quashing a sudden longing to rip down the barriers standing like unscaleable fortress walls between them. After this meeting they'd go their separate ways and there was no reason to suppose they'd ever cross paths again.

'Miss Alexander?'

Realising her thoughts had been miles—and years—away, Kaylie belatedly switched on her most alert expression and glanced towards the solicitor.

'Mr Johnstone?'

His lips quirked in barely hidden amusement. 'I wasn't sure you'd heard what I just said,' he remarked gravely.

'I may have missed a few words...'

'For God's sake, Kaylie!' Flynn all but spat the words, his features twisted in impatience. 'Can't you concentrate on anything for longer than ten seconds at a time? You were the same as a child—forever wool-gathering. You drove me crazy with it.'

Taken aback by his outburst, Kaylie could only stare at Flynn, astounded by the dark annoyance in his face. So she hadn't been listening—was it a federal crime all of a sudden?

'I sincerely hope you're not proposing to go through all that rigmarole again.' Flynn turned to the solicitor, his eyes narrowing.

Mr Johnstone fingered the knot in his grey silk tie, looking faintly uncomfortable. Clearly he wasn't accustomed to such scenes in his tranquil chambers. After a second he cleared his throat.

'I don't imagine it would matter greatly if I were to carry on,' he conceded with obvious reluctance. 'We haven't come to the main section of the will yet.'

Flynn sighed heavily. 'Then I suggest we get on with it,' he said, his cutting tones turning the request into a command.

For a fleeting moment Kaylie thought the solicitor would rebel, would refuse to toe the line Flynn was drawing so clearly. But though his already thin lips narrowed still further, he gave a tiny shrug, accepting the other man's superior strength of will.

'As you're both aware, Emma Anderson had no children and indeed no living relatives other than Miss Alexander——'

'Yes, of course we're aware of that, man, who would know it better?' Flynn cut in brusquely. 'Get on with it!'

Kaylie stared at him in unwilling fascination. When had he grown so arrogant? The Flynn she remembered had always been impatient, certainly, always in too much of a rush to get things done, but he'd never had this flint-edge to his character. She wondered again just what other changes the years had brought to the boy she'd once known better than any other living soul.

'As I was saying——' Mr Johnstone made a valiant bid to recover the situation and bring it back under his control '—Mrs Anderson had no offspring, no immediate or obvious heirs. In fact, she chose to leave everything she possessed to you, Mr Donovan, and to you, Miss Alexander.'

Kaylie felt the sting of tears behind her eyes and was forced to look away. That was so like Emma—even after her death she still wanted to put her warm, comforting arms round the two of them as she'd done so often in life.

'However . . .' Mr Johnstone paused and there was a faint, malicious gleam of amusement in his pale eyes as he focused on Flynn. 'However, there are certain conditions attached.'

'Conditions?' Flynn and Kaylie echoed the word together.

'What exactly do you mean?' Kaylie continued, ignoring the annoyed look Flynn sent in her direction.

Mr Johnstone sat back in his chair, clearly enjoying himself now.

'Well,' he began slowly, 'I mean that certain stipulations have to be met before the legacy can actually be shared out between you.' He paused again and Kaylie had the strangest feeling that he was playing with them, unlikely though such a frivolous act seemed in such a solemn man.

'Well?' Flynn all but exploded. 'What are the conditions?'

She noted with interest that he hadn't asked what the legacy was—so some things hadn't changed after all. Material possessions never had mattered to Flynn and it seemed that in some respects at least he was still the boy Emma had known. Despite herself, she felt a glimmer of the old affection for him.

'The conditions, Mr Donovan,' Mr Johnstone said slowly, refusing to be rushed, 'are quite specific, and they are as follows. You and Miss Alexander are to spend a period of time together.' He looked from one to the other with a wintry little smile. 'The will stipulates that you spend a month getting to know each other again. Should you refuse, the bequest will be made instead to a children's charity.'

CHAPTER TWO

'WHAT?' Flynn leapt to his feet, his blue eyes blazing. 'This is outrageous!'

'It's nevertheless quite true,' the solicitor returned calmly, steepling his fingers beneath his chin.

'I won't accept it.' As though unable to contain the restless anger surging within him a second longer, Flynn walked across the room to the big bay window, gazing sightlessly out over the road below. Behind him, Kaylie gave a tiny, silent gasp. He had walked with a very pronounced limp—a limp which seemed part of his natural gait, not just a temporary affliction. Her heart stilled— he'd always been so athletic, constantly on the move, searching for new challenges, new tests for his strong young body. Remembering the way he'd been, she could imagine the torment even this slight disability must have caused him. Was this the reason for his bitterness?

As if he'd read her mind, Flynn swivelled slowly round to face her, his eyes mocking as they met her own. He raised one eyebrow sardonically, but before he could say a word the solicitor began speaking again.

'Miss Alexander,' he said quietly, 'you haven't yet expressed your opinion on Mrs Anderson's will.'

She dragged her eyes away from Flynn, focusing with some difficulty on the other man, her thoughts still a dazed jumble.

'It's come as a bit of a shock,' she said, summoning up a smile. 'Frankly I can't even imagine at the moment how it could possibly be arranged, but if it's what Emma wished——'

'I won't have my life interfered with in this way.' Flynn's voice, low and savage, cut through her words. 'I refuse to allow Emma to dictate to me from beyond the grave.'

Kaylie flinched as though she'd been physically struck.

'How can you say such a thing?' She rounded on him, her eyes wounded. 'Emma gave us everything—both of us. She never dictated to us—she gave us freedom.'

'If I might perhaps make a suggestion?' Mr Johnstone cut in quietly. 'This has clearly come as quite a surprise to both of you—I don't think you should make a decision straight away, in the heat of the moment, as it were. Why don't you both go away and think about it for a while—perhaps talk it over together?' His lips twitched as if the idea amused him. 'Contact me again in a couple of days or so and let me know what you've decided.'

Kaylie nodded. 'I'll be quite happy to do that.' She slid a challenging sideways glance towards the man standing by the window, his profile stark and uncompromising against the light. 'What about you, Flynn?' she asked softly. 'Are you prepared to do this, at least? For Emma?'

For a long moment he said nothing, simply continued to stare through the glass. At last he turned on his heel and stared back at her, his eyes cold and unfriendly.

'Very well,' he said shortly. 'For Emma.'

The solicitor nodded in satisfaction. 'Excellent.' He rose to his feet, clearly relieved that the meeting was at an end. 'Then I'll bid you farewell for the moment and look forward to hearing what you both decide.'

He walked with them to the outer reception area, then, with the air of a man newly delivered from an ordeal, returned to his own office and closed the door firmly behind him. Kaylie took a deep, steadying breath and forced herself to look into Flynn's eyes, shrivelling a little inside at his forbidding expression.

'Perhaps we could talk about this over a cup of coffee,' she suggested diffidently.

He glanced at his wristwatch, scowling darkly. 'Frankly, I don't have time to waste. Thanks to your lamentable timekeeping, I'm already running late.'

She closed her eyes, mentally counting to ten as an answering irritation rose up within her.

'Then suggest a time which would be more convenient,' she said, striving to sound calm. 'You're clearly a very busy man. I'd hate to interrupt your schedule.'

His eyes narrowed and she felt a little twist of satisfaction, knowing he wasn't quite sure how to take her saccharine-sweet comment.

'I have a number of things to see to in town,' he said tersely. 'I'll meet you for a drink this evening.'

She pressed her lips tightly together, irritated anew by his cool assumption that she'd be free that evening.

'Unless that upsets plans you've already made, of course?' he continued, with a smoothness that set her teeth on edge.

'Unlike you, I'm prepared to be flexible,' she returned evenly. 'This evening will be fine.'

He nodded. 'I'm staying at the Denver. Be there at seven-thirty.' He turned on his heel then and the flame of anger that his last peremptory command had ignited died within her as she watched him limp away. As a young man his actions had been fluid, graceful as a cat's and with the same understated power. Now he was ungainly, and the sight brought an ache to her heart.

Needing time to think, she decided to walk home, though she'd never really enjoyed walking in Edinburgh, its busy streets and crowded pavements making her claustrophobic in a way empty skies and green fields never could. As a freelance photographer, working for a wide range of magazines and periodicals, her life over the past few years had been a nomadic one, and for the first time she found herself questioning the reasons that had made her set up base in the city. She'd been born there, of course, and spent her life there until the deaths of her parents and brother, but she'd never felt truly at home there, had never felt the affinity with the place that she'd discovered almost instantly in Emma's beloved Perthshire.

She'd moved back to Edinburgh to take the courses in photography necessary to turn a youthful hobby into a profession, then stayed on to establish contacts. Now, though, having built a reputation for intriguing, highly individualistic work, she could live wherever she liked. Maybe she'd think about moving out of the city—once she'd got this other thing with Flynn over and done with.

'Oh, Emma,' she murmured now, 'why did you do this to me?'

But how could she cavil at Emma's last request, when the woman had done so much, so very much for her? After leaving school Kaylie had been undecided about her future, torn between wanting to try out her wings and staying at home where she was loved and secure. And where she still had some connection with Flynn, even though he'd disappeared some time before. Emma had walked into her bedroom one day to find Kaylie staring out of the window over the lush green countryside beyond.

'Daydreaming, lass?' she'd said, with that soft, sweet smile of hers.

Kaylie nodded with a wistful little laugh. 'Just thinking how much I love this place.'

'It'll always be here, you know, even when you go away from it.'

'Will it?' Unconsciously Kaylie frowned, thinking of all the other things she'd counted on as constant in her life, only to have them disappear without warning. She raised anguished eyes to the other woman. 'Why did he go, Emma? Why did he leave us?'

Emma's smile was full of sympathy. 'Because it was time,' she said simply.

'But why?' All the agony of his leaving was poured into the two words. 'I thought we were so happy here, just the three of us. Why did he have to change everything?'

'Nothing can stay the same forever.' Emma's soft voice touched her like a caress. 'There were things he had to do—alone. Perhaps you'll only understand that when you leave too.'

Kaylie eyed her doubtfully. 'Then you think I should go?'

Emma regarded her steadily. 'I can't make your decisions for you, lass. You have to search in your heart for your own answers.'

In the event, leaving home hadn't been the ordeal she'd feared, largely thanks to Emma, who'd smoothed the transitional path as much as she possibly could. She'd suffered bouts of homesickness, but Edinburgh was only a short train ride away from Perthshire, and as the weeks passed she'd grown increasingly fascinated by the complexities of photography. Bright and lively by nature, she'd found no difficulty in making friends, but had shied instinctively away from any kind of romantic entanglements, even though at the time she hadn't really understood why.

Lost in her thoughts, she was surprised to discover she'd walked all the way home on automatic pilot, oblivious to everything around her. She let herself into the small town flat, half hoping to find it empty, since she really needed time to think, time to get her foolish thoughts straight in her own mind before she faced Flynn again. The sound of footsteps pounding through the hall from the kitchen told her she'd hoped in vain, and she closed her eyes briefly, preparing for the inevitable onslaught of questions. She wasn't disappointed.

'Well?' Hands on hips, a blonde Amazon stood before her, and Kaylie couldn't help but grin at the formidable picture her flatmate and best friend presented.

'Well what?' she hedged, making a valiant bid to play for time, even though she knew from past experience that it was pointless.

'You know very well, well what!' Brown eyes glared back at her. 'I've been waiting here for centuries—don't keep me in suspense any longer. Was he fat, bald and paternal?'

Kaylie looked away, but obviously not fast enough.

'Oh, lord,' the other woman breathed. 'He was gorgeous, wasn't he?'

'Not exactly, but——'

'You took one look at him and fell hook, line and sinker all over again, didn't you?'

'No, Beth, it really wasn't like that.'

'Then come through to the kitchen and have a cup of coffee and tell me just what it was like.'

Kaylie attempted to protest as Beth unceremoniously grabbed her by the arm and started dragging her along the corridor, but one look at her friend's determined face stayed her words. Beth in this mood wasn't to be thwarted.

'Now.' Beth pushed her on to one of the high stools, planted a mug of coffee in front of her on the breakfast bar, and stood back, folding her arms. 'Tell all. Was it a wildly romantic reunion? Did he take one look at you and breathe, "Oh, God, Kaylie, darling, why have we wasted so many years apart?"'

If the truth hadn't been so painfully different, Kaylie would have laughed at the hopeful expression in Beth's brown eyes. Instead she shook her head ruefully.

'I wish to heaven I'd never told you about Flynn in the first place,' she said. 'Then I wouldn't be facing this Spanish Inquisition now.'

Beth's eyes searched her face and after a long moment she frowned, the teasing light of laughter dying from her expression.

'He gave you a hard time, didn't he? Come on, Kaylie, out with it. I've known you for too long to be put off now. I saw the way you looked when you left the flat this morning—like an excited little kid heading off to a birthday party. Now you seem——' she paused, searching for the right description '—wounded, somehow.'

Kaylie gave a tiny shrug and reached for the coffee-mug. 'My own fault for entertaining expectations that couldn't possibly come true,' she said quietly.

'Why not?' Beth demanded. 'Why couldn't they come true?'

'Because the man I set out to see this morning doesn't exist any more.'

'Oh, love.' Beth laid a hand on Kaylie's arm. 'I'm so sorry. Do you want to talk about it?'

Kaylie glanced up, the irrepressible spirit of her humour pushing through the unhappiness. 'You mean I have a choice?'

Beth had the grace to look slightly sheepish. 'No. But I thought you might feel better if I let you think you had.'

Unthinkingly Kaylie pulled the band from her hair and started freeing her auburn locks from their imprisoning plait. 'That's better,' she sighed gratefully, running her hand through the rippling curls. 'OK, Beth, I'll tell you what happened. Then I want us both to forget about it and never bring the subject up again.'

Beth clicked her heels together and saluted smartly. 'Scout's honour.'

'Idiot.' Almost in spite of herself, Kaylie smiled, feeling a rush of fondness for the other woman. Beth at least knew the meaning of true and enduring friendship—Kaylie would stake her life on that. She took a sip of the hot, reviving coffee, then launched into the tale, her voice a little unsteady at first, but gaining in strength as she went on, resolutely leaving nothing out, even though the telling was far from easy. When she reached the end, there was silence for a long moment, then Beth slammed her empty cup down on the breakfast bar.

'The swine!' she said emphatically. 'The unbelievable swine! How could he be so callous?' She glanced at Kaylie curiously. 'Obviously you can't be expected to spend any time at all with an unfeeling pig like that. I take it you told the solicitor exactly what he could do with his will?'

Kaylie shook her head. 'I'll admit I was tempted,' she said. 'But I could never do it to Emma.'

Beth nodded understandingly. 'I suppose not. So what happens now?'

'The ball's in Flynn's court. It's up to him to decide whether or not he'll go along with the conditions of the will.' She paused, gazing thoughtfully at the smooth surface of the breakfast bar, without seeing it at all. 'I'm meeting him for a drink this evening.'

'You're what?' For a second Beth seemed frozen to the spot, then she leapt from the stool. 'Then what are you sitting there for? Get a move on!'

'Why? Where am I going?' Kaylie raised bemused eyebrows, taken aback by her friend's lightning change of tack.

'Into the bath, that's where, and then into the snazziest outfit we can concoct between your wardrobe—what there is of it—and mine.'

'Snazzy outfit?' Even after knowing Beth for several years, the blonde could still completely astound her on occasions, Kaylie thought dazedly, and this was obviously one of them. 'But why, for heaven's sake?'

'Because I refuse to let you go and meet him looking like a kicked puppy. Get the glad rags on, girl, and go out there with your head held high. Show that Mr High and Mighty Flynn Donovan just what Kaylie Alexander's made of!'

She was late. Again. With a despairing groan Kaylie glanced at her wristwatch as she entered the foyer of the Denver Hotel. It was all Beth's fault—if she hadn't insisted on personally supervising Kaylie's transformation, she could have been here ages ago. Now she'd doubtless incur Flynn's wrath all over again, for the second time in one day.

Still—a secret smile played about her lips as she remembered the last glimpse she'd taken in the mirror—she did look good. This morning, heading for the solicitor's office, she'd striven for an elegantly efficient look. Now, wearing a white cotton flying suit tucked into soft leather calf-length boots, a navy blue kerchief knotted rakishly about her throat, and with her newly washed hair tumbling in riotous curls about her heart-shaped face, she was barely recognisable as the same person. The flying suit was flattering to her slender, boyish figure and she liked the devil-may-care air it gave her, even if underneath it all she was far from feeling that way.

Yet why should she care so much? It was, after all, only Flynn she was meeting—Flynn, who before today had rarely seen her in anything but jeans and shorts or school uniform. She smiled mirthlessly, wondering just who she was trying to kid. The awful truth was that she was getting herself into a state simply because it *was* Flynn she was meeting. Even after the frosty reception he'd given her earlier, there was a part of her that desperately wanted him to look at her and see a woman, a beautiful, desirable woman, not just a freckled kid sister with patches on her knees and her head in the clouds.

Quaking inside, she walked into the hotel lounge, spotting Flynn instantly as he rose from his chair at a nearby table, his handsome features marred by a black scowl.

'For the second time in one day you choose to keep me waiting,' he said scathingly, and she flinched, her own words of greeting dying stillborn on her lips.

'I know, and I'm sorry,' she said, striving to keep her tone light.

'Been having a rest, have you?' His lips twisted contemptuously. 'Burning the candle at both ends, I suppose. Hitting the city's glittering night spots a bit too often, is that it, Kaylie?'

Considering she hadn't been near a night-club for months, and had no great liking for the places in any case, the accusation made her mouth quirk in wry amusement.

'Well, I——'

'Never mind.' He sat down and nodded curtly towards an empty chair. 'I have no interest in how you spend your life.'

'Gee, thanks.' Hurt by his brusqueness, she subsided into the chair. 'I suppose that at least means we won't have to waste any of your precious time by catching up on what's been happening to us both over the past ten years.'

His wintry smile got nowhere near his eyes. 'Correct.' He summoned a nearby waiter and placed an order for a Scotch and water. 'What will you have? A Coca Cola, perhaps—or are your tastes rather more sophisticated these days?'

If truth were told, a long, cold glass of Coke was just what her suddenly parched throat was longing for, and she'd never really developed a taste for alcohol of any description, but after that crack she wasn't about to admit it.

'I'll have a Campari, please,' she said, naming Beth's favourite tipple.

'Certainly, madam,' the waiter returned blandly. 'Would you care for anything in it?'

For a second she panicked, totally unable to recall what sort of mixer Beth used. Then she caught Flynn's knowing glance and tilted her chin defiantly.

'On the rocks,' she said blithely. 'And make it a double, please.'

Flynn's jet-black eyebrows rose derisively as the waiter walked away.

'My, my,' he said mockingly. 'The little girl really has grown up. Such sophisticated tastes nowadays.'

She shrugged. 'Perhaps I've had a chance to move in sophisticated circles since I last saw you.'

'Perhaps you have,' he returned musingly. 'And I wonder if the experience has done you any good at all.'

Stung by his words, she turned her face away, pretending to study the other customers in the lounge. They sat in silence till the waiter returned with the drinks and unthinkingly she took a generous mouthful of the red liquid, managing only with a supreme effort not to spit it straight back into the glass. Lord, her palate really must be uneducated, she thought wryly, summoning up a smile as she felt Flynn's eyes upon her.

'All right?' he queried.

'Delicious, as always.' And she took another sip to prove it. The flavour wasn't really unpleasant, she decided, just unusual—what would doubtless be described as an acquired taste. She'd just have to hope she could somehow acquire the taste some time between now and the bottom of the glass.

'So,' she said brightly, 'have you given any more thought to Emma's will?'

His brows drew together in a threatening frown.

'Enough to know it's completely unworkable.'

'But why?'

'Why?' His expression queried her sanity. 'Because even if I wished to, which I most certainly do not, I couldn't take time off to come and play at being a member of the Edinburgh jet set with you.'

'I see.' She dropped her eyes to the glass on the table before her, afraid he'd see the amusement in her features. Boy, was he ever in for a surprise if he ever did manage to bring himself to sample her lifestyle! Jet set it most certainly was not. 'But Mr Johnstone didn't say you'd have to come to Edinburgh,' she pointed out mildly. 'That's not one of the stipulations. I could come to your place instead.'

'Wouldn't that interrupt your schedule somewhat? Or would you simply have to ask your social secretary to rearrange a few appointments here and there?'

There was a definite sneer in his voice and she was forced to bite her lips to prevent herself from snapping right back at him. For reasons she couldn't fully comprehend she was becoming ever more determined to do what Emma had wished, but if she angered Flynn now there was no chance that he'd comply.

'Look,' she said, striving to sound reasonable, 'as it happens I do have a relatively clear stretch over the next few weeks.' That was twisting the truth somewhat since she'd promised a writer friend she'd check out some locations he wanted shots of for a series of articles he was planning, but she knew his schedule was flexible.

He sat back in his seat, a strange expression in his compelling blue eyes.

'My God,' he said slowly, 'you really are desperate to get your hands on Emma's legacy, aren't you?'

She flinched at the acid in his voice, cut to the heart by the accusation.

'Emma was good to me,' she shot back, her voice low and laden with anger.

'So good you couldn't wait to get away from her, back to life in the big city,' he jeered.

Her eyes widened in horror. 'That's not true! And, in any case, you left her first.'

'I had good reason,' he said shortly.

She eyed him consideringly. 'Did you really? And just what might that good reason have been?'

'That's none of your business,' he snapped back. 'It wasn't then, and it isn't now.'

Frustrated, she sat back with a disgruntled sigh. She'd asked Emma so many times why he'd left, only to be given the same answer, albeit couched in rather gentler terms.

'What's happened to us, Flynn?' she said quietly, suddenly weary of all the bickering. 'We were friends once.'

He shrugged uncaringly. 'You're talking about two different people. And a lifetime ago.'

'But what difference does that make?' The words were torn from her. 'Why can't we still be friends?'

His eyes, dark as the midnight sky, gazed back at her, their expression unreadable. 'You think it should all be so easy, don't you?' Mockery lined his soft Irish voice. 'You think we should simply be able to pick up again where we left off. What would you like to do, Kaylie—go for a ramble by the river, perhaps, or maybe have a picnic in the meadow?'

She shivered, remembering the times they'd done just that. 'Why not, if that's what it takes?'

His lips twisted irritably. 'Don't you think I was forced to spend enough time with you tagging at my heels like some kind of blasted puppy dog?'

'Forced?' Stabbed by his cruelty, she could only whisper the word.

'Sure.' The dark eyes hardened to jet. 'Baby-sitting was never my idea of a good time.'

'Then why did you do it?' She forced the words past a constricted throat.

'To pay my dues to Emma. She'd given me a home—it was only fair that I should share the chores.'

Kaylie looked away, gazing round the lounge bar without seeing a single thing. He was taking her most precious memories, grinding them beneath his heel into the dust like trash, and the pain was excruciating. She was gripped by a desperate urge to flee, to get away from the man so callously inflicting such agony, but, even as she made to rise, a picture of Emma swam before her eyes and she subsided back into her chair. For a long, endless moment she suffered the battle raging within, then at last looked back, steeling herself to meet his eyes.

'I would gladly walk out of this hotel and out of your life and never set eyes on you again,' she said, tightening her lips to stop them trembling. 'But I too want to pay my dues to Emma, and the only way I can do that is to go along with her last request. I wish I could do it alone, but that's not possible. I need your help—or at the very least your co-operation—no matter how grudged it may be.'

She thought she saw the faintest flicker of admiration in his eyes, but it was gone before she could be sure. And why should he admire her? she thought wearily—she was pushing against a brick wall that obviously wasn't about to give an inch.

'Very well,' he said abruptly, and she blinked in surprise.

'I beg your pardon?'

'You heard. For Emma and for Emma alone I'll go along with this fool-crazy scheme.' He picked up his glass and downed the contents in one quick swallow, then rose to his feet. 'Here.' He tossed a small white card into her lap. 'My address. Suit yourself when you arrive. It won't make any difference to me.'

She was still trying to find her voice to reply as he walked away, his limp more pronounced than ever.

CHAPTER THREE

KAYLIE gazed out over the open road, a small smile touching her lips at the sight of the lush green countryside spread out all round her. It had come as a surprise to discover that Flynn was still living in Perthshire, not many miles from Emma's farmhouse. There again, perhaps it wasn't really so very surprising, she reflected. He'd once told her he felt truly at home there, more so even than in his native Ireland.

She frowned, wondering yet again why Emma had always refused to tell her where Flynn had gone. His disappearance had been so devastating—Emma had tried to comfort her, had held her in a warm, consoling embrace, but she'd felt abandoned, just as she had when her parents and brother had died. In a way the grief had perhaps even been worse, because Flynn had in many ways taken the place of the family she'd lost, yet he'd gone of his own free will, had chosen to leave her.

'You'll always have me, love,' Emma had crooned softly into her hair, rocking her like a child as she sobbed her heartbreak. 'You'll always have me.'

But that hadn't been true either. Kaylie felt the sting of tears in her eyes, realising, maybe for the first time, just how alone in the world she was. How ironic that she should be travelling to spend time with the one person, other than Emma, she'd once truly believed would always be there for her. But those days were long gone. Flynn Donovan was a stranger now—and a hostile one at that.

Suddenly she was gripped by a strange reluctance to reach her journey's end, knowing that there she'd be forced to look into those devastating blue eyes and see only coldness where once there had been light and laughter—and a kind of love. She glanced at the map lying open on the passenger seat and realised she could only be half a dozen miles from Flynn's home. There was still time to change her mind—still time to head back to Edinburgh and ditch this crazy scheme of Emma's. Flynn would certainly be relieved.

Driving into a small village, she spotted a restaurant and on impulse drew to a halt, deciding to think things through over a cup of coffee.

The waitress, a plump middle-aged woman in tweed skirt and hand-knitted jumper, smiled welcomingly as Kaylie walked in.

'Now, then,' she said, leading Kaylie to a table near the window, 'what can I get you?'

'Just coffee, please.'

The woman frowned. 'Is that all? You look as if you could do with something more substantial. Have you travelled far?'

Kaylie shook her head, smiling inwardly at the woman's concern. It wasn't something you'd often encounter in a city restaurant, where the waiting staff were generally too rushed off their feet to notice customers as anything more than anonymous faces.

'Not far,' she returned. 'But I had an early start.' That was something of an understatement since she'd passed an entirely sleepless night, too keyed up by what lay ahead to rest.

'And I bet you didn't have any breakfast?' The waitress nodded knowingly.

'Well, I——'

'Just as I thought.' She pressed her lips together reprovingly. 'You young women are all alike; you just don't look after yourselves at all. Just look at you—slender as a reed. You must eat, you know!'

Kaylie felt a slight pang. She hadn't been mothered like this since Emma's death. She smiled. 'OK. I will have a snack.'

'Good.' The waitress bobbed her head in satisfaction, the tightly permed curls moving not a fraction. 'Some home-made soup and a few sandwiches, perhaps? Then maybe some hot apple pie to finish with? How does that sound?'

It sounded a lot more than a snack, but there was little point in arguing. Kaylie had lived in the country for long enough to know when she'd met her match.

'That'll be fine.'

The woman bustled away towards the kitchen, returning moments later with a bowl of broth and a plate of hot crusty rolls, laying them before Kaylie with a flourish.

'Now you tuck into that, my lass. You look as if you haven't had a decent meal in months.'

Kaylie opened her mouth to defend herself, then closed it again. It was true she was all too prone to living on snatched snacks, giving little thought to their nutritional value, but her type of work made that inevitable.

'So where are you going for your holiday trip?'

So much for her intention to have a quiet coffee and a chance to mull things over, Kaylie thought resignedly, realising the woman was disposed to chat.

'What makes you so sure I'm on holiday?' she hedged.

The woman shrugged. 'Well I know you're not a local, and if you were on a business trip you'd be using the motorway, so it's obvious you must be on holiday.'

Kaylie sipped the hot, succulent soup, giving herself time to gather her thoughts.

'I'm going to see an old acquaintance,' she said at last, realising this might just be a good opportunity to find out more about Flynn's life. 'Perhaps you know him—he's called Flynn Donovan.'

The woman grinned broadly. 'Well of course I know him,' she said. 'Everyone for miles around knows Mr Donovan.' The smile dipped slightly. 'For a while it looked as though he might really put our little bit of the world on the map, but that was before the accident, of course.'

Kaylie glanced up, the soup forgotten. 'Accident?'

'Of course, but you'll know all about that, being a friend of Mr Donovan's.'

'I've been out of touch for some time,' Kaylie said carefully. 'I knew something had happened to cause his limp, but I don't know the details.'

The other woman pursed her lips. 'Nor do I, to tell the truth. In fact——' she leaned closer, lowering her voice conspiratorially, even though they were alone in the room '—it's always been something of a mystery. All I can tell you is that Mr Donovan had been abroad competing somewhere, and doing very well by all accounts, when something happened, something that put him in hospital for several months. When he came back here, he was walking with a limp.' She shook her head regretfully. 'He seemed to change a lot after that. He'd always been so friendly and full of Irish charm, but after the accident he became all withdrawn—as though he was shutting himself away. And, of course, he hasn't competed since. Such a shame—we all believed he'd make it right to the very top, maybe even to the Olympics.' A smile lit her brown eyes from within. 'That would have been something, wouldn't it? An Olympic medallist in our little community?'

Kaylie gazed back in total confusion. Was it possible they were talking about two different people? Surely there couldn't be two Flynn Donovans in the area, both Irish and both walking with a limp? But Flynn had never been an athlete.

'Forgive my ignorance,' she said now with a light laugh, 'but what exactly did Flynn compete in?'

The waitress seemed surprised by the question. 'My goodness, you really have been out of touch with him for a long time, haven't you?' she said. 'Mr Donovan's an eventer—or rather, he was. One of the best horsemen in the whole country.'

*   *   *

The sign at the end of the road read: 'Cedar Wood Stables'. She'd arrived. Kaylie drew a deep breath, trying to steady the nerves churning within her, but without success. And yet, why should she be nervous? It was only Flynn she was going to see. 'Only Flynn'. The words echoed in her head like a mocking refrain. Learning of Flynn's near brush with greatness had come as a shock—why on earth hadn't Emma told her? Surely pride alone would have made her want to share Flynn's achievements with Kaylie? That she hadn't heard anything of his success for herself wasn't really surprising, since she'd never been particularly interested in horses, and knew next to nothing about the world of eventing.

Horses had, of course, been Flynn's passion for as long as she'd known him, but after one disastrous occasion when he'd given in to her pleading and taken her riding, only to have her fall off and break her arm, he'd always refused to take her again.

She drove slowly along the farm track, her eyes drawn to the fields on either side. There were horses everywhere, it seemed. Tall, long-legged creatures raising their heads to gaze with liquid-eyed curiosity at her car, one, rather bolder than the rest, cantering over to the hedge, tossing its mane contemptuously.

They were a breathtaking sight, their coats gleaming conker-bright in the early summer sunshine, and for a moment she was strongly tempted to stop the car and grab her camera. She resisted the urge with an effort—now she was so near she couldn't keep putting the dreaded moment off for ever.

She still wasn't a hundred per cent sure she was doing the right thing in coming at all—talking to the garrulous waitress in the restaurant had tipped the balance, had excited her curiosity, but even now she'd gladly reverse all the way back up the drive and head for home.

With a resigned sigh she turned into the farmyard and drew slowly to a halt. For good or evil, she was here now. There could be no backing out—and, in any case, the one thing she'd never be accused of was being a quitter. No matter how difficult the photographic assignments she'd been given in the past, she'd always stuck with them to the bitter end, and that was a matter of personal as well as professional pride. She'd simply have to apply the same sort of thinking to this.

She stepped out of the car and was instantly surrounded by a swarm of laughing-faced dogs, their tails swishing in welcome.

'Well, hello, boys.' She stooped to stroke one of the animals, laughing when another promptly jumped up and planted its paws on her leg.

'Jet! Mungo! Get down immediately.'

Hearing the voice of authority, the dogs instantly deserted her and she looked up with little surprise into Flynn's blue eyes. With a sinking feeling she recognised the look of cold hostility she'd been dreading.

'You didn't have to do that,' she said quietly. 'They were only being friendly.'

'It seems my dogs can't distinguish between welcome and unwelcome visitors,' he said curtly as the animals fawned lovingly round his legs.

His words hurt as he'd obviously intended them to, but not for worlds would she have given him the satisfaction of knowing that.

'If you're this pleasant to all your visitors, I'm surprised you have any at all,' she returned tartly.

She spotted a flash of surprised amusement in his eyes, but her tentative smile drew only a thunderous frown in return.

'Come on,' he said shortly. 'You may as well come into the house and find yourself some- where to sleep.'

She looked about her interestedly as he led her through a big, old-fashioned kitchen dominated by a huge range and a broad, scrubbed-wood table, then on to what was obviously the living- room. The furniture was worn and shabby, but the room was clean and welcoming with its sagging armchairs and sofa, and a sheepskin rug on the carpet before the fireplace. She spotted a vase of flowers on the window-sill, the blooms prettily arranged, and jealousy squirmed worm- like within her at the obviously feminine touch. Saying nothing, she followed him towards the staircase, irritated by her own reactions. He was a good-looking man—had she really expected to find him living the life of a cloistered monk?

'You might as well have this room.' He stopped at the top of the stairs, throwing open the first door in a row of four. 'You'll find bedding in a linen cupboard at the end of the corridor.'

The room was small and designed for practicality rather than comfort, furnished only with a narrow single bed, chest of drawers and a wardrobe.

'Not exactly what you're accustomed to, I imagine?' One jet-black eyebrow raised sardonically.

Since the demands of her job had accustomed her to living in everything from a tent to a luxurious mansion, there really wasn't a truthful answer to that, so she simply smiled.

'Not exactly.'

He shrugged uncaringly. 'If it doesn't suit you, you can book into a hotel. I'll be happy to recommend one.'

She closed her eyes briefly, a spurt of anger flaring up inside her. Did he really have to make it so very obvious just how much he didn't want her there? Strangely, his attitude simply strengthened her own resolve to stay, though she couldn't have explained why, even to herself.

'This will be just fine,' she returned with a calmness she was far from feeling. She lifted her bags and walked past him into the room, then stood for a moment looking out of the window, enjoying the sight of the Ochil Hills in the distance.

'That damn will,' he said bitterly. 'I wish to God I knew what Emma was playing at when she concocted the blasted thing.'

Kaylie turned to face him, taken aback by the unhidden savagery in his voice.

'Perhaps it was because she remembered the way you and I once were,' she said quietly.

'The way we once were?' He crossed the room towards her, his leg dragging, and she felt a faint tingle of alarm as he towered over her, his dark eyes glittering malevolently. 'And how was that, Kaylie?'

'We were friends.' She stood her ground, fighting an urge to back away from him, even though inside she was quaking. 'We cared for each other.'

'Ah, yes.' His voice lowered and he brought his hand up to her face, stroking her cheek with long, cool fingers. 'I remember the way you cared for me, Kaylie. I remember the way you tried to flaunt your teenage body in front of me.'

'That's not true!' She was horrified by the very suggestion. 'I never did any such thing.'

'Didn't you?' His hand pushed through her mane of hair to clasp the back of her neck and she shivered, repelled by the caress that had no warmth or affection in it, yet at the same time astounded to discover just how much she longed for his touch. 'Perhaps your memory isn't as good as mine.' He bent towards her, his face coming closer and closer, his breath warm on her skin, and she could only gaze up at him, hypnotised by his very nearness. 'And now you're no longer a child.' The soft Irish voice went relentlessly on and she shuddered, helpless under his spell. 'By now you must have learned all the things you could only wonder about back then.' He looked at her consideringly. 'Perhaps we should make good use of our unwanted legacy— let me discover just how good a pupil you've turned out to be under someone else's tutelage.'

'No, Flynn,' she moaned, but he ignored her entreaty, pulling her round to face him, and even as she tried to struggle, his lips found hers. It was a harsh, uncaring kiss, his mouth hard and demanding as it moved over hers, yet, even as she tried desperately to push him away, his touch ignited a molten river within her and she groaned helplessly. His hands moved restlessly over her body and she tried to squirm away, yet knew she was having to fight herself as much as him, knew that even in this callous embrace she was more alive than she had been in years.

From somewhere deep inside she finally found a hidden reserve of strength to wrench her mouth from his and looked up into his fathomless blue eyes, her lips swollen by his angry kisses, her breathing fast and uncoordinated.

'I don't know what you think you're doing.' She bit out the words. 'This isn't what I came here for.'

'No?' He raised his eyebrows in lazy mockery. 'I'm relieved to hear it.' He dropped his arms, abruptly releasing her, and it was all she could do not to fall without the support of his hard body. 'You're not my type, anyway.' His eyes ran over her slender form and she suffered agonies beneath his scrutiny. 'Too thin,' he continued harshly. 'When I hold a woman in my arms I want to feel a woman's body, a woman's curves, soft and desirable.'

She shuddered, lashed by the contempt in his scathing words, but managed with difficulty to stand her ground.

'If you'll be good enough to point out the linen cupboard, I'll get on with making this place habitable,' she said quietly. 'I'd like to unpack and settle in.'

'Sure you can manage such a domesticated task all by yourself?' He regarded her blandly. 'I'm afraid I don't have a maid I can call on to assist you.'

'I think I can cope,' she returned, refusing to rise to the bait. Then she slid him a curious glance. 'But surely you don't run the house as well as the stables?'

He shook his head impatiently. 'Hardly. I have a housekeeper who lives nearby. And the stable girls help out when required.' He eyed her coldly. 'But don't expect any of them to start running round after you. They've got quite enough to do as it is.'

'I didn't mean . . .' She shrugged helplessly. He was obviously determined to read the wrong thing into everything she said, so there seemed little point in trying to set the record straight.

'And while we're on the subject, I'll expect you to pull your weight while you're here.' He smiled unpleasantly. 'I've got no room for slackers or time-wasters. If you want to earn your bed and board, you'll be expected to do your bit along with the rest.'

'I'll be more than happy to lend a hand round the house,' she began, but he shook his head.

'That's not what I meant. Mrs MacDonald is perfectly capable of keeping things running smoothly in here—but we're short-staffed in the stables. One of the girls has gone down with flu, so an extra pair of hands will come in useful.'

'Work with the horses, you mean?' She gazed at him in astonishment. 'But I've never done anything like that before.'

'Then I hope for your sake you're a fast learner.' He crossed the room towards the door, turning back to add a parting shot. 'Don't worry, Kaylie, it's only for a few weeks. Even your lily-white hands should survive that much work.'

CHAPTER FOUR

LEFT alone, Kaylie sank down on to the bed, unconsciously raising her fingers to her lips, still feeling the imprint of his kisses burned on to her soft mouth like a brand. In the old days he'd often kissed her, light, brotherly little caresses dropped on to her nose or her hair, but this had been like nothing she'd ever experienced before. It was as though he'd deliberately been trying to hurt her, she thought wonderingly, unable to understand why. The Flynn she'd once known would never have hurt her—would never willingly have hurt anything. What had happened to change him so much? Why did he now seem to dislike her so intensely?

The worst thing of all was that he *could* hurt her, she acknowledged ruefully—she might manage to put on a brave face before him, pretending his barbs were simply bouncing off her skin, but she couldn't lie to herself. Where Flynn was concerned, she was as vulnerable as a newborn kitten and just as susceptible to pain. His attack had wounded her deeply, the more so because it had followed his kisses, ungentle though they had been.

She shook her head, giving up the struggle to understand. He was an enigma—perhaps she'd never really make sense of him, and the sooner she accepted that, the better for all concerned.

While she was here she'd simply have to keep her head down, work hard enough to keep him off her back, and generally get through the days as best she could.

Feeling a little calmer, she slid off the bed and made her way along the corridor, finding the linen cupboard behind the last door. With her arms full of bedding she was about to head back towards her room when a young blonde woman appeared at the top of the stairs, her attractive features marred by a frown as she spotted Kaylie.

'What are you doing here?' she asked sharply. 'You should be down in the stable yard with the others.'

'Others?' Kaylie stared back uncomprehendingly.

'The other stable girls, of course,' the woman returned impatiently. Her frown deepened to a scowl as she took in Kaylie's load of sheets and blankets. 'What are you doing with those?'

'I'm just about to make up a bed.'

'For whom?'

'For myself.'

The blonde seemed taken aback and distinctly less than pleased. 'For yourself? You mean you'll be living in?'

Kaylie nodded. 'Yes.'

'Damn Flynn.' The woman seemed to be talking to herself as much as to Kaylie. 'He didn't tell me about this. He's never had staff living in before.'

'But I'm not staff,' Kaylie offered helpfully.

The woman's brown eyes narrowed. 'Then who the hell are you?'

Kaylie opened her mouth to reply, then closed it again, realising she wasn't too sure of the answer to that one. She could hardly call herself a friend, she thought regretfully. Under the circumstances, friendship was the last thing she could claim with Flynn.

'Look,' she said, 'do you mind if I dump this stuff in my room? I'm going to drop it all over the floor in a moment.'

The other woman followed her, her eyes sweeping over Kaylie's luggage.

'Would you mind telling me just what this is all about?' she said testily. 'Flynn hasn't mentioned anything to me about having a house guest.'

Kaylie studied her, wondering just who she was and why Flynn should need to tell her anything about his domestic arrangements. 'Perhaps he simply forgot,' she suggested mildly. 'Does it matter?'

The woman gave a haughty sniff. 'Flynn and I are partners,' she said curtly. 'I don't appreciate his keeping me in the dark.' She paused, her brown eyes coolly assessing Kaylie. 'Even over trivial issues.'

As a put-down it didn't even have the saving grace of subtlety and it was all Kaylie could do not to flinch visibly. She returned the woman's cool stare, steeling her own features to remain expressionless. So this was Flynn's partner—but in what sense? She was undeniably attractive— the jodhpurs and sweat-shirt she wore did nothing to disguise her curvaceous figure and long, shapely legs. With a pang she remembered

Flynn's gibe about her own slender form. The blonde was much more to his taste—he'd certainly know he was holding a woman if she were in his arms. With a sick feeling in her stomach she turned away, pretending to busy herself with the bed.

'Perhaps you should talk to Flynn about my presence here,' she said at last. 'I'm sure he'll be able to explain.'

'He'd better.' With that she turned on her heel and strode from the room.

Kaylie heaved a deep sigh. Dear heaven, what was she doing here? More and more she was being made to feel like a cuckoo in the nest, nothing more than an unwanted imposition.

'Oh, Emma,' she murmured quietly to the empty room, 'you'd never have wished this on me if you'd known what it was going to be like.'

Not relishing another encounter with Flynn or his glamorous partner for the time being, she stayed in her room for the rest of the afternoon, trying to read a book, but in reality taking in not a single word, even though she'd been engrossed in the story just a couple of days before. She was still there when she heard footsteps on the stairs some time later, followed by a peremptory rap on the door. Before she had time to answer Flynn appeared in the doorway, his eyes narrowing as he saw her stretched out on the bed, the open book in her hand.

'Having a nice, lazy time, I see,' he said caustically. 'I don't suppose it occurred to you that we could perhaps do with a hand down in the yard?'

Kaylie laid down the book. 'I'm sorry,' she said evenly. 'I thought I might get in the way if I started wandering about. I thought——'

'You thought!' He shook his head in exasperation. 'Do me a big favour, Kaylie, and don't bother thinking any more while you're here. Just do as you're told without question and then your presence might not be a complete waste of space.'

'Now wait a minute!' She bridled at his autocratic tone, needled by his arrogant assumption that she was there simply to be ordered about. 'I didn't come here to be your damn lackey!'

His lips curled in sardonic amusement. 'Then what did you come for, Kaylie? A nice little holiday in the country? An amusing break from the constant round of socialising in the city? You'd better forget that idea straight away, because I won't have free-loaders in my home.'

'Look,' she said, deliberately keeping a tight rein on her growing anger. 'I've already told you I'm more than happy to do my bit around the house, but since I've never worked with horses I can't simply pitch in. I could easily do more harm than good, through sheer ignorance.'

He shot her an incredulous look. 'Did you really think I would let you loose among my animals? Frankly, Kaylie, I value them far too highly for that.' He smiled coldly. 'Tomorrow morning you can learn about the joys of stable management, starting with mucking out. Even you should manage that.'

He was deliberately trying to demoralise her, she realised, but she wouldn't give him the satisfaction of knowing he'd succeeded. She swallowed the cutting retort she would have loved to fling back at him in that moment, satisfying herself with a single grim nod. 'Fine.'

'Right. I've come to tell you it's dinnertime in five minutes. Sorry to disappoint you, but this country estate doesn't run to a cocktail hour first.' His dark eyes flickered over her corduroy trousers and light sweater. 'And don't bother to change. We don't stand on ceremony round here.' He turned to go, but swung back as an afterthought occurred. 'And don't upset Amanda while you're here.'

'Amanda?'

'My partner. She's none too happy at the thought of my having another woman under my roof.'

'Although of course you informed her she had no cause for concern.' Kaylie said it before he could, unwilling to give him yet another opportunity to put her down.

His eyes gleamed. 'I'd have thought she'd have realised that for herself as soon as she saw you,' he said with quiet malevolence. 'But women are always irrational.'

His words stabbed home as she knew they'd been intended to, but she kept her returning gaze steady.

'Then there's no problem, is there?' She paused, eyeing him curiously. 'I can't help being surprised, though.'

'Surprised?'

'To find you under a woman's thumb.'

His look of fury gave her a fleeting moment
of triumph. At least she'd managed to score a
single point in this war between them.

'I'll never be under any woman's thumb,' he
gritted out. 'But Amanda and I have developed
a good working relationship since we've been in
partnership. I don't intend to let you put a
spanner in the works.'

Kaylie sighed morosely as he left the room. So
she had Amanda's enmity to contend with as well
as Flynn's. Was she fated to remain entirely
friendless in this house? Right then she'd have
given a great deal just to hear a friendly word or
see a welcoming smile. Perhaps the stable girls
would prove more amiable.

That hope died as soon as she went down to
dinner and felt the full force of five hostile glares
turned in her direction. She'd anticipated that
from Flynn and Amanda, but it was dishearten-
ing in the extreme to see the same expression of
dislike mirrored on the faces of the three young
stable girls.

'Good evening,' she said brightly, refusing to
let herself be cowed by the icy atmosphere.

'Sit down,' Flynn ordered curtly. 'Mrs
MacDonald refused to serve up till you'd arrived.'

Kaylie took the place he'd indicated beside
Amanda and smiled pleasantly at the three girls
ranged along the opposite side of the table.

'Sorry I've kept you waiting,' she said. 'You're
probably all starving after a hard day's work.'

With one accord the trio glanced uneasily
towards Amanda as if seeking permission to re-
spond. Apparently none was forthcoming for

they made no reply. One at least had the grace to look slightly embarrassed, Kaylie noticed, a sweet-faced, slightly plump girl with long dark hair pulled back in a pony-tail.

The connecting door to the kitchen swung open and everyone looked up in relief as the portly figure of the housekeeper appeared, bearing a steaming cauldron of thick, succulent stew. She placed it in the centre of the table, then bustled away again, reappearing a moment later with servers of potatoes and vegetables.

'It looks great, Mrs Mac.' Flynn looked up with a grin that went straight to Kaylie's heart. Smiling at the housekeeper, his eyes warm and with that mischievous twinkle she remembered so vividly, he looked just like the Flynn of old. Would he ever look at her like that again?

Mrs MacDonald folded her arms over her ample bosom and gave a satisfied little nod.

'Aye, well, it'll help keep the wolf from the door, I dare say.' Her eyes focused on Kaylie. 'You'll be Miss Alexander,' she said. 'Seems we'd better introduce ourselves since everyone here has apparently lost their manners.'

Kaylie felt a wave of gratitude wash over her. At least one person in the household was predisposed to be civil.

'I'm Kaylie,' she returned warmly. 'Not Miss Alexander.'

The older woman smiled. 'And I'm Alice MacDonald, known to just about everybody as Mrs Mac. You just come and tell me if there's anything you need.'

'I will.'

'Good. Now tuck in, lass—if I know this crowd there'll be nothing left in a few minutes, so don't bother overmuch about being polite.' She gave Kaylie a friendly wink and returned to the kitchen.

That little exchange had boosted Kaylie's spirits considerably, but her heart sank all over again as she turned her attention back to the table and saw the identical expressions of annoyance worn by Flynn and Amanda. The young girl with the pony-tail was smiling, but the smile vanished instantly, as if she'd been caught in the middle of doing something reprehensible.

Amanda dished up the stew, passing plates along the table in silence. Her task done, she turned to Flynn, blatantly shutting Kaylie out.

'I'm still not happy with Buster,' she said. 'He's got no flair at all.'

Flynn frowned consideringly. 'It's a mystery. He comes from good jumping stock and he certainly showed potential when I first saw him.'

'I think he's lazy.'

Flynn shook his head. 'I don't think so. Last time I watched him I thought he seemed a little afraid of the jumps for some reason.' His attention focused for the moment on Amanda. He failed to notice two of the stable girls exchange a look, but Kaylie spotted it and also saw Amanda's eyes narrow as she glanced across the table.

'There's no reason for him to be afraid,' she said firmly. 'He's treated with consideration, just as all the others are. Isn't he?'

The girls nodded, but said nothing. Kaylie carried on eating as though paying no attention, but made a mental note. Something was going on here that Flynn wasn't aware of. It was none of her business, of course, and Flynn would doubtless be the first to tell her so, but, even if only through a misguided sense of old loyalties, she owed it to him to keep her eyes and ears open while she was under his roof.

The rest of the meal passed uneventfully, and Kaylie helped the girls clear the table and wash up while Flynn and Amanda took themselves off to the office to go over stable accounts.

If she'd hoped the girls might relax in her company away from Amanda's eagle eye, however, she was doomed to disappointment. In the kitchen they chatted to one another, but pointedly excluded her from the conversation, although again she had the impression that the dark-haired girl was uncomfortable with the situation. Eventually she decided to take the bull by the horns, tired of the exclusion zone they seemed to have created around her.

'Right,' she said, letting the soapy water drain away from the sink. 'You all know my name. For the next few weeks you're going to have to put up with the fact that I'll be around the stables, probably getting under your feet every time you turn around, so I'd better know your names so at least I'll know who I'm apologising to.'

They slid sideways looks at one another, clearly unsure what to do, then the dark-haired girl smiled.

'I'm Laura,' she said, with a slight touch of defiance. 'This is Jan.' She indicated the girl who'd been drying the dishes, a small, slender brunette with wide green eyes, who offered a tentative smile. 'And this is——'

'Claire.' The third member of the trio spoke up for herself. 'I'm Amanda's cousin.'

That piece of information was clearly intended as some kind of warning, Kaylie recognised, seeing the strangely challenging look in the girl's close-set hazel eyes. She made no comment, however, but simply smiled, glad to have cracked the ice at least, even if she hadn't broken it altogether.

'Are you going to be working with us?' Laura asked curiously.

Kaylie nodded with a self-deprecating little smile. 'That's the theory. But I've never worked with horses before, so I'll have to depend on all of you to keep me on the right lines.'

Claire gave a snort of disgust. 'Never worked with horses before? Well, don't expect me to baby-sit you. I've got better things to do with my time. Come on, Jan, Laura—we'd better check the horses before we go.'

Jan obediently scuttled after her, but Laura lingered after they'd disappeared.

'Pay no attention,' she said. 'Claire thinks she's the bee's knees because she's related to the boss, but she's nothing special.'

'Related to the boss?' Kaylie frowned. 'But Flynn's the boss, surely?'

Laura nodded. 'Sure he is, but Amanda sees to most of the day-to-day stuff.' She seemed to be weighing Kaylie up as she spoke. 'She's not at all pleased you're here. She came roaring into the stable yard after she saw you in the house. We thought she was going to have a blazing row with Flynn there and then, but he managed to calm her down.'

'How long have they been partners?' Kaylie queried.

'Since Flynn's accident. At first she took over the running of the yard while he was in hospital, then when he came home she stayed on.'

'Does she work directly with the horses?' Kaylie asked the question as offhandedly as she could, but Laura's expression grew guarded.

'I'm sorry, but I'll have to go, or Claire will run telling tales to Amanda that I've been letting them do my work.' A quick, flashing grin lit her face and Kaylie felt a rush of liking for the youngster. 'Look, you can work with me to-morrow morning, till you get the hang of things, OK? I'll keep you straight.'

'I'd love that,' Kaylie returned gratefully.

'Right, then. I'll see you in the stable yard at six.'

CHAPTER FIVE

KAYLIE hadn't expected to see Flynn again that evening, assuming he'd be embroiled in the stable books for hours on end, so she was taken by surprise when he walked into the living-room some hours later to find her comfortably ensconced in one of the sagging old armchairs, re-reading the chapters of the book she'd completely failed to take in earlier.

'Put the television on if you want,' he said and she jumped at the unexpected sound of his voice. 'I'm not so tight-fisted I begrudge the electricity.'

It was the closest he'd come to making a civil comment since her arrival and, try as she might, she couldn't prevent a ridiculously pleased smile from curving her lips as she looked up at him. Dressed casually as he was in old corduroy trousers and a cotton shirt left undone at the throat, his black mane rumpled as though he'd been distractedly running his fingers through it, he was still the most beautiful man she'd ever seen and she was forced to steel herself against the rush of pleasure his presence gave her.

'I'm not really a great television fan,' she said softly.

His lips twisted cynically. 'I don't suppose your lifestyle would leave time for such innocent pursuits,' he said and she frowned, puzzled by the cryptic remark. After a minute she shrugged. He seemed to have a completely false idea of the way she lived, but, stubborn as he was, there seemed little point in trying to put him straight. He'd believe what he wanted to believe.

'I generally take a walk round the stables about this time just to check everything over,' he went on. 'Want to come?'

That casual 'want to come?', offhand though it had been, made her heart miss a beat. It was an echo of the past—the same phrase he'd used to invite her along on a thousand and one expeditions, and she'd always fallen over herself to accept, much to Emma's amusement. Even now, as a supposedly mature adult, she still felt the old rush of childish excitement, and she had to work hard to reply in the same, seemingly indifferent tone.

'Sure. I might as well get the lie of the land before tomorrow morning.'

She followed him out of the house and down the lane leading to the yard, her eyes widening in pleasure at the layout. It was obvious where Flynn's priorities lay—his house might be shabby and in need of decoration, but his stables were immaculate, the paintwork gleaming, the yard itself swept perfectly clean.

Several horses stuck their heads over the half-doors to inspect their visitors, whickering softly in welcome as they recognised Flynn. He moved from one box to the next, talking softly to each animal, running his hands over their legs and scratching their necks. Kaylie followed him in silence, content simply to watch the man with his horses. That he loved each one was clear even to

her inexperienced eye—and they obviously
adored him, each one rubbing its velvety nose
against his hand.

The summer evening air was still warm, the
scent of nearby flowers mingling with the stable
aromas, and she drank it in deeply as though it
were costly perfume. In that moment she felt
happy, though the emotion was tinged with a
peculiar melancholy. She'd spent so much of her
life longing to be with Flynn again, and now she
was—but this Flynn was a stranger.

'Which one is Buster?' She forced the words
past a throat grown suddenly constricted, as he
left one box and bolted its door securely.

'This fellow here.' He pointed to the last horse
in the row. 'Come in and meet him. He's a gentle
big soul.'

'Big being the operative word,' she murmured
dubiously, following him into the loose box and
very nearly backing straight out again. Buster was
enormous—the largest horse she'd ever seen other
than heavy shires and Clydesdales. Flynn looked
at her with an amused grin.

'Buster's a lamb. He wouldn't hurt you.'

'I'm delighted to hear it,' she returned drily,
nevertheless maintaining a respectful distance
between herself and the equine giant, who merely
glanced at her in mild curiosity as Flynn stroked
his neck. 'Does he belong to you?'

Flynn's mouth tightened grimly. 'I wish he did.
Buster is owned by an Edinburgh businessman
who wants his property to be permanently in the
medals.'

'And Buster isn't?' Mustering her courage, she took a couple of steps forward to stroke the animal's nose, smiling in delight as he nibbled with incredible gentleness on her fingers.

'Not at the minute,' Flynn returned shortly. 'But I'm still convinced he will, given time.' His dark brows drew together. 'The horse just isn't happy for some reason, and that's why he isn't performing as he could and should be.'

'Off colour, perhaps?' she ventured.

Flynn threw her a scornful look. 'Does he appear off colour to you?'

She stood for a moment in silence, studying the animal. Little as she knew about horses, she'd have to admit he seemed in peak condition, his rich chestnut coat gleaming with good health, his kindly brown eyes alert and bright.

'He looks absolutely wonderful,' she said at last. 'What makes you so sure he isn't happy?'

Flynn shrugged his powerful shoulders. 'Intuition.' He gave a faintly rueful smile. 'Or perhaps just my own stubborn refusal to accept I could possibly be wrong about any horse.'

That admission of his own fallibility was the first chink she'd seen in his armour of arrogance and she wanted to reach out to touch him, to stroke the pain away as he'd done for her so often in the past. Only fear that he'd reject her sympathy kept her immobile and silent. After a moment he bent to run his hands down Buster's legs and she knew a pang of regret for the opportunity lost and her own lack of courage. She'd missed a chance to bridge the yawning chasm between them—and who knew if the chance would ever come again?

'What the hell——?'

His angry exclamation startled her out of her reverie.

'What is it?'

'Scars on his legs. Here, feel this.' She felt a strange tingle in her skin as he reached for her hand, guiding it with his own to a place on Buster's foreleg, just below the knee. Gently moving her fingers, she felt the roughness of a healed-over cut.

'It's not serious, is it?'

'Not in itself, no,' he conceded with a frown. 'But I'd like to know how it got there all the same.' He shook his head angrily. 'Probably one of the girls—they do a lot of the exercising and they're supposed to stick to a set pattern of work, which doesn't include jumping unless it's under my supervision—or Amanda's, of course. If they've been hurtling him round cross-country jumps, so help me, I'll...' He let the threat hang in the air unfinished, and Kaylie felt a quick rush of sympathy for Laura and the other girls if they should be found guilty. Flynn in avenging mood would not be a pretty sight.

'Which horse do you enjoy riding most?' she ventured, hoping to distract his thoughts.

He gave her a slightly pained look. 'I don't ride any of them.'

'You don't?' She was completely taken aback by his reply. 'But I thought you trained them.'

He sighed heavily, clearly exasperated by her ignorance.

'I do. From the ground. Amanda rides them over the jumps.'

'But why...?'

The black look on his features told her she was venturing into dangerous waters without a life-jacket and she bit her lip, wishing she'd never begun the conversation.

'Why don't I ride?' The vivid blue eyes pierced her with their burning intensity. 'Because, Kaylie, I am lame. Or hadn't you noticed that?'

'Of course I'd noticed,' she returned in a low voice. 'But I hadn't realised——'

'Well, you realise now,' he cut in savagely. 'So perhaps you'll refrain from asking any more damn fool questions.' He limped out of Buster's loose box and she followed, aching for the man in his anger. Not pity—his arrogance made such an emotion unthinkable—but a hollow feeling of regret for all that he had once dreamed of, only to have it snatched away. Riding had always been so important to him—it must have torn him apart to lose it. That was clearly another reason for the bitterness he wore like a cloak, and the realisation made her sick at heart.

Back at the house he headed towards his office after muttering a grudged, 'Goodnight. Don't sleep in.' After a moment's indecision she turned towards the stairs, deciding she might as well go to bed. In the old days she'd have followed him, wouldn't have thought twice about invading his private sanctum and forcing him to open up to her. Such candour had been the privilege of childhood, she thought ruefully. Adults were expected to respect each other's need for privacy.

But, oh, how she'd longed to follow that re-
treating back.

Lying in bed, she gazed unseeing into the
gloom, her thoughts a confused jumble whirling
in her restless mind. She'd been under his roof
for less than a day and already he'd thrown her
emotions into a maelstrom. In a few short hours
she'd experienced everything from downright irritation at his high-handed treatment to sweet joy
when for just a fleeting moment it seemed as
though they could still recapture the relationship
of old.

Uttering a deep groan, she turned over in bed,
thumping the blameless pillows as if it were all
their fault. Since she was generally possessed of
a fairly even-tempered, sweet-natured dispo-
sition, no one had ever been able to affect her in
the way Flynn could, his attitude determining her
own mood, sending her from blissful heights to
agonising depths in the flash of dark blue Irish
eyes. She could try to convince herself it was just
because of their shared history, but in her heart
of hearts she knew it wasn't that easy.

The real truth lay in one simple, inescapable,
dreadful fact. As a youngster she'd hero-
worshipped him, seeing no faults in her idol. Now
she could see the faults, but her feelings hadn't
changed one iota. The juvenile crush was in very
real danger of deepening into something much
more serious. If she wasn't extremely careful, she
could find herself in love with Flynn Donovan.

She barely slept that night, partly through fear
of incurring Flynn's wrath all over again by over-

sleeping, but mostly because her mind refused to switch off, replaying everything that had happened over and over like a video behind her tired eyes. Somewhere in the night she'd reached a decision, she realised as she dragged her unwilling body from bed at what seemed like an inhumanly early hour.

Facing up to the truth of how she felt about Flynn had been painful but unavoidable, and, having done it, she had to decide how to deal with it. Clearly, for the sake of her own pride and peace of mind, she could never let him know, but she was only too aware of her own inability to dissemble. She'd been told all too often by teasing friends that she'd never make a poker player, for her feelings tended to shine all too clearly in her large, expressive grey eyes.

Well, for once in her life she'd have to become a good actress, she swore silently, pulling on a pair of jeans and a bulky sweat-shirt. It would probably be the hardest thing she'd ever done, but as far as Flynn was concerned she was little more than a nuisance in his life, and she couldn't bear to see understanding dawn in his eyes, followed inevitably by scorn.

The stable yard was already a hive of activity when she arrived and Flynn greeted her with no more than a cursory nod.

'Find Laura,' he said curtly. 'I understand she's volunteered to take you under her wing, lord help her.'

Kaylie managed not to flinch at his entirely humourless snub, instead tugging an imaginary forelock.

'Yes, sir, boss, sir,' she returned solemnly, trying not to grin as he scowled darkly in reply.

'Look, Kaylie,' he said, making no attempt to disguise his impatience, 'working with the horses isn't a game. I'd be obliged if you'd try to remember that, and endeavour not to get under the girls' feet.'

Nettled, she glared back at him. 'Despite what you seem to think, I'm no longer the child you used to order about,' she said tightly. 'I fully appreciate the fact that this isn't a game, and I'm equally well aware of my own inexperience where horses are concerned. But you're the one who insisted I work in the yard.'

'Only because I'm short-staffed,' he shot back.

'Which isn't my fault,' she returned firmly. 'Now I'm more than willing to do my bit, but I'm not willing to be treated like an idiot.' Even as she stood her ground, she was quaking inside. It wasn't that she was afraid of Flynn, she told herself resolutely as his eyes darkened in annoyance, just that it went against the grain of the close, easy relationship they'd once shared to argue with him. But she couldn't simply keel over and let him walk all over her, no matter how much it pained her to take a stand now. 'At least credit me with a modicum of common sense,' she finished.

'You'll have to prove you have some first,' he returned swiftly. 'And believe me, I'll be keeping an eye on you. Don't expect any favouritism from me—if you make any mistakes I'll come down on you like a ton of bricks, just as I would with any of the stable girls.'

Favouritism! As tense and tied up in knots as she was, she was hard pressed not to burst out laughing at the very notion of Flynn doling out any special favours to her. She sent him a wry look. 'I think you've already demonstrated that.'

He gave a single curt nod. 'Right. Now go and find Laura. There's no time to stand around talking.'

It was on the tip of her tongue to remind him that he'd been the one doing most of the talking, but she bit the words back. Things were going to be difficult enough without getting involved in a wrangle with Flynn every few minutes. But if he thought she was going to accept his every command and insult like a meek little girl he had another think coming, she pledged silently as she stalked off across the yard. He wasn't the only one who'd changed over the years—working in the highly competitive field of freelance photography had forced her to toughen up considerably too. She wasn't the adoringly pliable teenager he'd once known. And maybe he'd discover that for himself.

Laura was in the feed room, measuring scoops from various bins into plastic buckets, and she looked up with a welcoming grin as Kaylie walked in.

'Morning,' she said cheerfully.

'Is it?' Kaylie groaned. 'My protesting body's still convinced it's the middle of the night.'

'You'll get used to it. Now, if I show you where the hay's stored, and explain how much each horse gets, do you think you could fill the nets for me?'

'Reckon I could just about manage that.'

'Good. Come with me.'

If she'd considered herself relatively fit and strong, Kaylie quickly came to the conclusion that morning that she must be badly out of shape. She was kept hard at work, with no quarter given for her inexperience. Friendly though Laura was, she clearly expected Kaylie to pull her weight, and when they went into the farmhouse a couple of hours later for breakfast she felt as though she'd already done more than a full day's graft.

'How are you enjoying life as a stable lass then?' Mrs Mac asked as Kaylie dropped gratefully into a chair.

'Ask me that tomorrow—if I'm still alive, that is!'

'Proving too much for a soft city kid, is it?'

Kaylie looked up into Amanda's coolly mocking eyes, unable to miss the note of malice in her voice.

'I wouldn't go that far,' she said mildly. 'I'm simply not accustomed to lugging full water pails around, or hefting loads of wet, dirty straw into sacks. I'll get used to it.'

Amanda smiled, but without warmth. 'From what Flynn tells me it must be something of a novelty for you to get your hands dirty.'

Kaylie mentally counted to ten, remembering with irritation Flynn's command not to 'upset Amanda'. She'd like to do a lot more than upset her, she thought grimly, hating the blonde's patronising sneer.

'I have been known to do the odd spot of physical work from time to time,' she returned amiably. 'Though of course my line of business really requires brain rather than brawn.'

The spark of anger that flared in Amanda's brown eyes told her she'd hit the mark, but out of the corner of her eye she saw Flynn's lips tighten irritably and her heart sank. Was he really so besotted with the blonde that he'd take umbrage on her behalf every time Kaylie defended herself?

'What is your line of business?' Laura asked interestedly, but Amanda cut in before Kaylie could open her mouth.

'Never mind that now,' she said sharply. 'Get on with eating and cut the chatter.'

Kaylie reached for a slice of toast, more to keep her mouth occupied than because she really wanted it. For two pins she'd have snapped back at Amanda, cutting her down to size. Only the fact that she was Flynn's partner kept her in check. It wouldn't do the yard any good at all to have two females constantly bickering at each other's throats. But how could he have chosen to work with such a harridan?

She sent the other woman a glowering look across the table, all but choking on a mouthful of toast as she spotted the warm smile Amanda was bestowing on Flynn—a smile, furthermore, that was being returned in full measure. It seemed that glowing blonde looks and a curvaceous figure were more than enough to compensate for a sharp tongue, where he was concerned, at least.

She swallowed hard, fighting a wave of jealousy as burning as acid. She was being ridiculous, she told herself firmly. As a teenager she'd felt possessive where he was concerned—this was simply a left-over from those days when she'd had to grit her teeth every time he took a girl out. Well, she was a big girl now—surely mature enough to cope.

After breakfast she was set to work grooming one of the quietest horses, a task she found herself enjoying even though she'd approached it with some trepidation.

'Ginger's a poppet,' Laura had told her re-assuringly. 'He'll probably go to sleep while he's being strapped.'

'Strapped?' Kaylie's eyes opened wide. 'You mean I've got to hit the poor animal?'

Laura chuckled delightedly. 'Don't be daft! Strapping just means a thorough grooming. It's easy—just be sure to use plenty of elbow grease.'

After strapping for what seemed like an eternity, Kaylie began to seriously doubt whether her elbow and indeed the rest of her arm would ever recover from the exertion. She was taking a quick breather when Flynn appeared at the door of the box.

'Managing OK?'

She jumped at the unexpected sound of his voice, and quickly resumed brushing. She wasn't about to let him accuse her of slacking.

'Fine, thanks.'

'No, you're not.' He pushed the door open, muttering irritably under his breath. 'Look, the whole idea of strapping isn't just to clean the horse, but to tone up their muscles. It should be a massage as much as anything. You're just tickling his skin with that brush.'

To her astonishment he grabbed hold of her hand with the brush still in it and started stroking the bristles firmly over Ginger's rippling chestnut coat. Her fingers grew strangely nerveless within his grasp, her instinctive words of protest dying stillborn in her throat as he moved to stand behind her, his powerful frame mere centimetres from her own.

'This is how I want you to do it,' he said and his breath, warm and minty, murmured over her skin, making her tremble deep inside. 'Put a bit of force behind each stroke of the brush.' He'd rolled the sleeves of his white cotton shirt up to the elbows and her eyes were riveted helplessly to the sight of his tanned, muscular arm with its lavish sprinkling of black hair, as it moved against the horse's silken skin.

'Flynn, I...' Her voice faltered as she turned her head to look at him, then promptly wished she hadn't as she realised his bent head was close to her own. With just the slightest of moves she could be in his arms, pressing her own hungry body into his, drinking in the potent unmistakably male smell of him. The longing to do just that was more intense than anything she'd ever known, and she was forced to close her eyes for a second, desperately trying to bring her senses under control once more. When she opened them again it was to see Flynn's vividly blue eyes gazing at her with an expression impossible to decipher, and her lips parted in unspoken and unconscious invitation as her will to fight silently dissolved.

'My, my, isn't this a cosy little scene?' A shrill voice rang out behind them and Kaylie's heart froze within her as she turned to see Amanda by the door, her brown eyes blazing with anger. 'Is this how you instruct all the hired hands, Flynn?'

'Did you want something, Amanda?' His voice was icily impatient and Kaylie felt a new wave of despair wash over her. She'd almost rather have heard him apologise, or make excuses to the other woman. At least that would have shown he was embarrassed at being caught red-handed. Instead he was merely irritated by the suspicions she was making no attempt to disguise, which made it patently obvious that, as far as he was concerned, there was nothing to be suspicious about.

For a second Amanda seemed taken aback, then she shook back her long blonde mane contemptuously as her eyes flickered dismissively over Kaylie. 'Only to tell you that Claire has Julius ready for you in the arena,' she said with a trace of petulance. 'I assume you want to work him yourself?'

'You assume correctly,' he returned evenly. He released Kaylie's hand and the brush she'd been holding fell to the ground from her suddenly numb fingers. Almost in a daze she watched him leave the loose box without another word.

'I suggest you take that ludicrously lovelorn look off your face.' Amanda turned on her as soon as Flynn was clearly out of earshot, her rather narrow lips thinned to a spiteful white line. 'I can see perfectly well that Flynn was merely trying to speed up what would otherwise have been a long and laborious procedure if left entirely to you.'

Inside her heart was thudding erratically, but Kaylie managed somehow to conjure up an uncaring shrug. 'Why bother to mention it, then?' she said calmly. 'Or is it yourself you're really trying to convince?' She bent to pick up the brush, but not before she'd seen the look of sheer malice contorting the other woman's features. If Amanda had possessed a dagger she'd probably have had it thrust between her shoulder-blades, Kaylie realised with a shudder.

'You've groomed the damn animal for long enough. Get him tacked up now. I haven't got time to stand about waiting all day.'

The brush in Kaylie's hand stilled in mid-stroke and she turned slowly back towards the door.

'Tacked up?' she echoed disbelievingly.

'Well, of course. Or did you expect Ginger to saddle himself?' Amanda shook her blonde head disgustedly. 'I suppose you're going to tell me now you don't know how to tack up.'

Kaylie couldn't suppress a wry little smile. 'Got it in one.'

'Not the sort of task one would normally have to undertake in the salons and night-clubs of the big city, I suppose?'

Kaylie screwed up her eyes in puzzlement. Just what was that supposed to mean? 'No. I don't suppose one would,' she said at last, giving up the struggle to understand. There was no way she was about to give Amanda the satisfaction of asking her to explain.

Amanda gave a little grunt of annoyance. 'Oh, for goodness' sake—just get out of here and find some menial little task that even you can perform without botching it. I haven't got time for this.'

'Can you manage to tack up for yourself?' Kaylie returned swiftly with a saccharine-sweet smile. 'Or shall I get one of the other stable hands to do it for you?' Not waiting for an answer, she dropped the brush into Amanda's hand and sauntered out of the box. It was only as she was striding away that she felt a wave of misery obliterate the tiny moment of triumph she'd experienced on seeing the other woman's impotent fury. What was happening to her? She'd never been catty or bitchy in her life, yet Amanda seemed to bring out the worst in her. She really wasn't proud that she'd allowed herself to descend to her level—yet what else could she do?

The question was still plaguing her mind as she heard her own name being called and turned to see Flynn waving from the exercise arena.

'I'm just about to put Julius here through his paces,' he said, indicating the sturdily built grey horse at his side. 'But he works best with a bit of bribery and I forgot to bring any pony nuts. Go and get me some, would you?'

'Nuts?' She gazed back uncomprehendingly and he sighed.

'Not real nuts,' he said with exaggerated patience. 'Horse nuts. They're used as part of the feed and occasionally as a treat. They're in one of the big black bins in the feed room. One of the girls will show you which one.'

In the feed room she found Claire scrubbing out pails she'd used earlier. When Kaylie ex-

plained what she wanted, the other girl's eyes
narrowed.

'You're taking them to Flynn?'

Kaylie nodded. 'He's working with a big grey
horse. Julius, I think he said.'

Claire pointed towards the back of the room.
'The end bucket,' she said shortly. 'Put a few
scoops into a pail.'

Bucket in hand, Kaylie returned to the manège,
intending simply to hand it over to Flynn, then
return to the stables. However, he was already
working the horse, standing in the centre of the
ring, sending it round him on a long rope, occasionally flicking a whip behind the animal to
encourage him on, and almost without realising
what she was doing she clambered up on to the
wooden rails, fascinated by the scene before her.

'What are you doing?' she asked interestedly.

'It's called lunging,' he returned. 'It's part of
the basic training.'

Once again she wished she had her camera to
hand—normally it never left her side, but she'd
felt she could hardly lug the equipment round
the stables. Perhaps later she'd fetch the gear—
if Flynn didn't object. A faintly rueful smile
touched her lips—these days Flynn seemed to
object to the very air she breathed, so his ap-
proval seemed unlikely.

She lost track of time as she sat there, watching
man and animal working in harmony. Flynn
never raised his voice once, yet the powerful grey
obeyed his every command. There was a very real
bond between them, she realised, and it was that

intangible element she'd somehow love to capture on film.

At last he gave the command to halt and walked towards Julius, gathering up the lunge rein as he went.

'Bring the bucket here,' he said. 'He's worked well this morning; he deserves his reward.'

She did as she was bid, but just as she held the bucket up to the horse Flynn knocked it violently from her hand, his sudden movement making Julius throw his head back in alarm.

'You bloody stupid little fool!' he spat viciously. 'This is sugar-beet!'

She stared back at him in confusion.

'Don't you know you could kill a horse by giving it sugar-beet like this?' He lifted a handful of the spilt feed, thrusting it angrily under her nose. 'This stuff has to be soaked in water for twenty-four hours—if it's fed dry it swells up in the horse's stomach.' His eyes were almost black with fury as he glowered down at her. 'I thought I told you to ask one of the girls where the nuts were kept.'

'She did.'

They turned to see Claire leaning over the post and rails, the glint in her eyes a clear indication that she was thoroughly enjoying the show-down.

'She asked me, Flynn.' She gave a little shrug. 'I pointed out the bin to her.'

Flynn swung back on Kaylie, his dark eyes gathering together thunderously. 'And you managed to muck up even that?' He shook his head in sheer disbelief. 'You're not fit to be around horses. You could have killed this animal.'

'Then why didn't you have the bins labelled if one contained a potentially dangerous feed?' Kaylie yelled back, her own temper rising to match his.

'Because it never occurred to me that I'd ever have an idiot working in the yard.' He handed the lunge rein over to Claire. 'Here, you look after Julius. And make sure he gets the proper feed.' His gaze flickered over Kaylie and she felt something shrivel deep inside at the clear contempt in his eyes. 'As for you,' he said quietly, 'just stay out of my sight. Right now I can't trust myself not to give you just what you deserve for that little stunt.'

He stalked away towards the house, his limp as much in evidence as ever as Kaylie stared after him.

'You really did it this time.' There was undisguised glee in Claire's mocking tones. 'Just wait till Amanda gets wind of this—she'll probably insist Flynn sends you packing, and good riddance too.'

All too aware that she was clearly in the wrong, Kaylie couldn't even defend herself against the younger girl's scathing attack. As Claire led Julius from the ring, she turned back towards Kaylie, her lips twisting scornfully. 'You're not wanted here,' she said witheringly. 'And the sooner you leave, the better it'll be for all of us.'

Left alone, Kaylie wandered morosely over to the fence and sat down with her back against one solid post. Accustomed to the plaudits of success in her own career, she couldn't ever remember being made to feel so small, so worthless. It was a deeply unpleasant sensation. But how could it have happened? In her mind she replayed the scene in the feed room—had she misheard Claire's instruction? Or—a frown puckered her brows—had the girl deliberately sent her to the wrong bin, knowing what the outcome would be? But why should she? What could she possibly have to gain?

Kaylie remembered her malicious look of triumph and the crowing note in her voice when she'd anticipated Amanda's reaction. Of course, she was Amanda's cousin. Had she recruited Claire in some kind of vendetta? The notion seemed both ludicrous and perfectly feasible at one and the same time. But why bother? Amanda must know by now why she was here, and even if she was jealous of the old friendship between Flynn and Kaylie she must surely have realised by now that none of the old affection still endured.

Kaylie picked disconsolately at a tuft of grass, feeling a new rush of unhappiness at the memory of Flynn's white-lipped anger. It seemed she was destined to keep annoying him at every turn. It hardly mattered that she might actually be blameless, that she might have been a victim of Claire's manipulation, for that possibility obviously hadn't even occurred to him. He'd been only too willing to believe the worst of her. There seemed little point in trying to protest her innocence, even if she could. The harm had already been done.

CHAPTER SIX

KAYLIE deliberately steered clear of Flynn for the rest of the day, unable to face the inevitable contempt in his eyes. Laura set her to work cleaning tack, and although the chore was both boring and laborious she was glad of it, for hidden away in the tack room there was no risk of bumping into Flynn accidentally.

To her amazement, Amanda had proved surprisingly understanding, seeking Kaylie out later in the afternoon to say, 'It was a stupid thing to do, of course, but fortunately no harm's come of it. Just be more careful in future.' Kaylie was so taken aback that she didn't even reply, simply stared after the shapely blonde as she left the room. She'd expected outright censure from that quarter, not a mild reproof. So why was she left with a niggling feeling of suspicion? Why couldn't she accept what the other woman had said at face value?

Because the atmosphere here was making her paranoid, she decided gloomily, bending once more to the task of rubbing saddle soap into a leather bridle. In comparison with Flynn, Amanda had been positively gracious. She should accept that in the spirit it had apparently been given, not go searching in her mind for ulterior motives that probably didn't even exist.

Pride alone carried her through the ordeal of dinner, tilting her chin upward and injecting a note of light-heartedness into her voice that was very far from what she was really feeling deep inside. But even as she ploughed on with her act of bravado she wasn't really sure why she was doing it. Flynn barely glanced in her direction during the whole meal, and when he did his expression was forbidding. As usual Laura and Mrs Mac were the only two who seemed to accept she was actually a human being, and whenever they left she felt bereft, abandoned in a lonely and deserted place.

After the meal Flynn disappeared into his office and the girls left with Amanda, only Laura bothering to say goodnight. Kaylie wandered through to the living-room and threw herself down in an armchair before the television, too unsettled even to read.

'Good programme?'

The unexpected sound of Flynn's voice at the door some time later startled her and she looked up with a sinking feeling, wondering what was about to hit her next.

A faint smile played about the corners of his mouth.

'I thought you didn't enjoy television much.'

'I don't. But this is an excellent programme. One of my favourites.' It was a complete lie since she'd barely taken in a word that was being said on screen, but she didn't want him to realise she'd been brooding.

He raised one eyebrow. 'Really? Then you can fill me in on the plot so far. Perhaps I'd enjoy watching it too.'

For a second she floundered, knowing only too well that she couldn't even have named the programme, let alone described the plot.

'I don't think so,' she managed at last. 'It's not really your cup of tea.'

'Nor yours, either,' he murmured drily, taking a couple of steps into the room. 'Unless you've developed a late interest in steam trains.'

Completely caught out, she felt a ridiculous urge to giggle, but stifled it ruthlessly. Once they'd have laughed at such a thing together, but now that would probably open the way for another attack from his barbed tongue. Instead she shrugged with as much nonchalance as she could muster.

'You've got no way of knowing what my interests are these days.'

His eyes darkened. 'True. Nor do I care.'

She looked away, stabbed by his casual cruelty. 'What do you want, Flynn?' she asked in a low voice. 'Have you come to give me another lecture? Wasn't this morning's sufficient?'

Even though she wasn't looking at him, she could feel the heat of his annoyed glare.

'Listen to me,' he said through gritted teeth. 'You need considerably more than a lecture. Frankly I'd like to put you over my bended knee and tan your hide for what you did today.'

Goaded by a sudden rush of fury, she leapt to her feet, her eyes blazing. 'Lay one finger on me and you'll regret it,' she swore. 'I'm not the little girl you used to order around any more.'

His lips twisted savagely and for a desperately unnerving moment she thought he would strike her. Instead his fingers curved round her chin, pressing cruelly into her jaw.

'No, you're not,' he said in a voice that was quiet, yet laden with venom. 'That little girl was sweet and innocent. Oh, she could be mischievous at times, but there was no malice in her soul.'

Although she'd steeled herself for whatever he was about to say, Kaylie couldn't help but flinch.

'Malice?' she echoed disbelievingly. 'Is that what you think prompted this morning's mistake?'

'What else could it be? You call it a mistake, yet Claire swears she showed you the correct bin. If it wasn't malice, then it was crass stupidity— and whatever else you may be, Kaylie, my darling, you aren't stupid.'

The endearment, spoken in his soft Irish voice, yet carrying nothing but contempt, made her shudder. To her horror she felt the sting of tears in her eyes, but when she tried to look away his fingers held her fast.

'Don't call me that,' she said, her voice low and uneven.

'What—"my darling"?' He said the cruel words again, his delivery slow and deliberate. 'But why not, Kaylie—you used to like it when I called you that. Don't you remember? You used to blush. You had quite a schoolgirl crush on me then. It was really quite endearing.'

She wasn't blushing now—instead her face was deathly white, all of its natural colour drained away as his taunting continued.

'Things were different then,' she said, forcing the words past dry lips. 'I was a child.'

He seemed to consider her words, then nodded. 'Yes, I suppose you were. And what about now, Kaylie?'

'What about now?' She shot him a blazing look, her eyes full of the pain he was inflicting so wantonly. 'Now I'm an adult, and I can see through adult eyes, thank God. I can see you for the arrogant, bad-tempered swine you really are.'

His fingers pressed harder still into her tender flesh till she almost cried out.

'Arrogant and bad-tempered, am I?' he said with a quiet malevolence that made her flesh creep. 'And yet I can still make you tremble just by touching you. Why is that, Kaylie?'

'Because you infuriate me beyond all reason,' she ground out, making one last desperate attempt to wrench herself free. 'If I tremble when you touch me it's because I'm discovering just how deeply I loathe you.' Her words were meant to hurt him the way he'd been hurting her, but to her despair she saw only mocking amusement in his blue eyes.

'Are you really so sure of that, Kaylie?' he murmured. 'Does that mean that if I were to kiss you now you'd tremble out of sheer dislike for me?'

The very idea of his kissing her was enough to make her go to pieces inside, but she stood her ground, glaring back at him with as much venom as she could muster.

'That's exactly what it means,' she hissed.

'Shall we put it to the test?'

'No, Flynn!' But even as she made the desperate plea her eyes were closing helplessly as his face shadowed hers, her lips parting of their own free will to welcome the marauding touch of his mouth, and she groaned agonisingly as his arms closed about her like steel bands, imprisoning her against his powerful chest.

She wanted to protest, wanted to rebel against his easy domination of her spirit, but her body disobeyed the frenzied commands of her brain, her will to fight paralysed by the overwhelming need flooding her veins. There was no tenderness in his caress, no gentleness in the mouth plundering her own, yet she hungered for more, unconsciously driving her fingers into his thick black hair to pull him closer, closer still.

At last he released her, pushing her away, his face a frozen mask of contempt as she stumbled without his support.

'Damn that blasted will of Emma's,' he gritted out. 'I wish I'd never even met her if it had to mean having you forced upon me all over again. Surely once in a lifetime is enough for anyone!' He turned on his heel then and she slumped into an armchair, unable to bear the weight of the pain any longer.

'Oh, Emma,' she murmured brokenly to the empty room, 'why did you do this to me? Couldn't you just have left me with my foolish dreams of the way things used to be?'

*   *   *

Kaylie woke the next morning with a smile on her lips, stretching contentedly as she rolled over to switch the alarm clock off. It was only when she opened her eyes to see the bleak, inhospitable little room that her smile fled and reality crashed in on her like a heavy weight. She'd been dreaming, she realised—dreaming of happier days when she and Flynn had walked hand in hand, laughing with the ease of close, comfortable friends. Days that would never come again, and that awful truth closed in on her, suffocating the quiet joy she'd awakened with.

Slowly, dispiritedly she rose from her bed, moving on automatic pilot as she made her way to the bathroom to wash and dress for the day ahead—another day which promised only to alienate her still further from the man who'd once meant so much to her. That thought made her give a bitter little laugh—the agonising truth was that he still meant everything in the world to her, despite all. If he didn't, this ordeal wouldn't be half as difficult.

She took a deep breath before walking into the stable yard, vainly attempting to quell her nerves. It was a feeling she wasn't accustomed to—oh, she'd been nervous before, when she was facing up to a difficult photographic assignment, for instance, but then there had been exhilaration along with the nerves, not this gut-wrenching anxiety that threatened to rock the very foundations she stood on.

Intending to seek out Laura, she headed for the tack room, only to find Flynn and Amanda standing very close together, and the sight made

a dull, heavy weight form in the pit of her
stomach. A strangely detached part of her photographer's mind was able to appreciate the
picture they made—he so tall and commanding
with his raven-black hair and vivid blue eyes, she
so curvaceous and feminine, her bright golden
hair tumbling over her shoulders as she gazed up
at him. Then as one they turned towards her and
she suppressed a shudder at their shared expression of irritation and thinly veiled dislike.

'So you've managed it again, Kaylie.' Flynn
shook his head disgustedly as though he could
barely believe it himself.

Even though she felt more like weeping, Kaylie
mutinously squared her shoulders, refusing to let
either of her accusers see her looking cowed.

'Good morning to you too, Flynn,' she said
with a faint touch of disdain. 'May I enquire as
to just what I've "managed"?'

'This for a start.' Amanda thrust a bridle
towards her. 'And this for a close second. I
haven't dared check the others yet.'

Kaylie stared uncomprehendingly at the tack
she was holding, recognising the leather-work
she'd laboured over the previous day.

'The bridles are twisted,' Amanda said
patiently, as though explaining to a backward
child. 'Why didn't you ask for help if you weren't
sure how to put them back together properly?'

Taken aback by the surprisingly understanding note in the other woman's voice, Kaylie
could only stare at her speechlessly.

'It's a common fault among total beginners,'
Amanda continued, laying one hand on Flynn's

arm as though to placate him. 'Don't you remember, young Claire once tried to put a bridle
on Ginger that was practically upside-down.'

'I didn't leave the bridles like that,' Kaylie cut
in, finding her voice at last. 'I did put them
together properly.'

Flynn's blue eyes flickered over her. 'So you
can't even own up to your mistakes,' he said
coldly. 'Are you trying to suggest someone came
along in the night and deliberately sabotaged your
handiwork?'

That was exactly what she would have liked to
suggest, but the forbidding expression on his
tightened features warned her not to bother. He'd
never believe her anyway. That realisation made
her stomach muscles clench painfully—the Flynn
of old would never have doubted her word. Now
it seemed he was determined to believe the worst
of her at every turn.

'All right, Kaylie,' Amanda said quietly, 'if I
can possibly find time later I'll give you a quick
lesson in the reconstruction of tack.'

'Don't bother,' Flynn said abruptly. 'You've
got more than enough to do around here without
having to play nursemaid. Especially today.' His
eyes bored into Kaylie like gimlets. 'I'm going to
be away from the yard for most of today. Try to
stay out of everyone's way, Kaylie—you're
nothing but a damned nuisance.'

She stood rooted to the spot as he pushed past
her, Amanda following in his wake. Then she
heard the sound of the blonde woman's laughter
ringing out in the yard, and a shudder coursed
through her body. How had it happened? She

picked up the two bridles Flynn had been holding, gazing at them as though they could tell her the answer.

It just wasn't in her character to be so unforgivably slapdash—normally she was conscientious and thorough in her work, no matter how mundane the chore. But, she remembered miserably, yesterday her mind had been full of the incident with the sugar-beet and Flynn's blistering anger, so perhaps she had been distracted enough to muck up the simple task.

She was still trying to work it out when Laura appeared at the door.

'Don't take it to heart,' she said and Kaylie's heart sank still further as she realised everyone in the yard must know about her latest *faux pas*. 'Come on—the hay nets need filling. If we don't feed these animals soon, they'll be reporting us to the RSPCA.'

Kaylie smiled, grateful for the warmth in the younger girl's voice, even though it was galling in the extreme to know that by now she must be an object of ridicule to the others.

'Think you can trust me?' she said with a rueful little smile. 'Are you sure I won't fill them with straw or something even worse by mistake?'

Laura chuckled. 'Worse things have happened at sea,' she said. 'And in this yard, come to that. Don't worry—Flynn's bark is a lot worse than his bite. He'll have forgotten about it by the time he gets back this evening.'

If only she could be as confident, Kaylie thought grimly, following the other girl towards the barn. This latest mishap would simply count as yet another black mark in her already tarnished record where Flynn was concerned.

'Where's he going?' she asked, more for the sake of conversation than because she really wanted to know. At this moment she'd be glad to hear he was heading for a three-week vacation in the Bahamas—at least she wouldn't run the risk of incurring his wrath all over again.

'He's heard about a promising young horse down in the Borders,' Laura explained, bending over to cut the string from a bale of hay. 'He's going to take a look.'

'Will he buy the horse if it's any good?'

Laura shrugged. 'Depends.'

'On what?'

'The price. If it really is promising then it'll cost. A lot.'

'But surely it would be a worthwhile investment?'

Laura sent her a curiously assessing sideways glance, then rocked back on her heels, her eyes unusually serious.

'Flynn's had a run of bad luck,' she said carefully. 'With horses like Buster, who should have turned out to be blue-chip certainties, but for some reason or other have failed to live up to his expectations.'

Laura was clearly doing battle with her conscience, Kaylie realised with swift insight— wanting to confide, yet unsure how much she could safely say to someone who was, to all intents and purposes, a stranger to the yard—and a proven ham-fisted one at that.

'Is it as simple as that?' she said offhandedly, beginning to stuff hay into a net. 'Pure bad luck, I mean?'

Laura's expression grew guarded. 'What else could it be?' she hedged.

Realising she'd be unwise to push too far too fast, Kaylie gave a quick self-deprecating grin. 'How should I know? I can't even put tack back together.'

Clearly relieved, Laura laughed, her eyes dancing with mirth. 'Nor fill a hay net! Look, you're spilling most of that on the ground. Come on, give it here—I'll hold it open; you shove the hay in.'

Laura's words played in her mind all through breakfast. For some reason she was suddenly convinced there was more to Flynn's problems than simple bad luck. Laura's caginess was the main clue, though she'd have bet her last dollar that the friendly youngster wasn't personally involved in anything underhand. Kaylie had always prided herself on being a good judge of character, and she was as certain as it was possible to be that if something was going on behind Flynn's back Laura had nothing to do with it. But she knew something about it—or, at the very least, had strong suspicions.

She shook her head, vainly trying to rid her mind of its crowding doubts. She was probably way off base, she decided, watching Amanda's full red mouth curve into a smile at something Flynn had said, and feeling a twist of acid jealousy deep down inside. After all, what did she know about horses? If Flynn was content to explain things away as bad luck, then who was she to go searching for answers that probably didn't even exist, except in her own unhappy mind?

But even as she tried to do battle with her own instincts, she knew she was destined to lose. No matter how badly he treated her, she still cared for him, still couldn't bear to see him hurt. He wouldn't thank her for interfering, she acknowledged grimly, but, even if it meant risking his wrath and his scorn all over again, still she had to try.

Strangely strengthened by her new-found resolve, she returned to the stable yard after breakfast with a new sense of purpose, and when Flynn stuck his head round the tack-room door to say goodbye she was able to nod coolly at him without experiencing the sense of inferiority and uselessness that had been dogging her over the past couple of days.

A faintly ironic grin touched his lips as he saw the tangled tack in her hands. 'Having another shot?' he queried drily. 'Try concentrating this time, Kaylie. You might find it works wonders.'

'Have a good trip,' she returned evenly, refusing to let his words rankle. 'I hope it's a successful one.'

As though sensing something different in her attitude, he eyed her curiously. 'Want to come?'

The throw-away invitation made her heart still within her, her hands trembling as she began unbuckling one bridle. She glanced up, seeing the same surprise mirrored in his dark eyes, and the breath caught in her throat. He'd amazed himself, she realised—as though for just a split second the old carefree Flynn had pushed through the barriers this cold and distant man had set about himself. She felt the prickle of tears behind her eyes and looked away, terrified he'd see her moment of weakness.

'Thanks,' she managed at last. 'I'll stay around here if you don't mind.'

'Mind?' The harshness was back in his voice as though to negate his lapse and she winced inwardly. 'I simply thought it might save Amanda and the girls from having to bail you out of any more mistakes if I got you out of their hair for a while. God knows they don't need you around here—any more than I do.'

'You think it's a pleasure for me?' The anguished retort was spoken almost before she had time to think. She glared back at him, angered as much by her own inability to keep quiet as by his cruel gibe. 'I didn't ask to be here any more than you asked to have me. I'm here for Emma's sake, that's all. If it weren't for her, I'd leave this terrible place right now, and very happily never set eyes on you again. You're not the only one who wishes she'd never made that will—but she did, and I for one am determined to see it through, no matter how much of a swine you are.'

He took a step forward, his features tightening angrily, but she managed with an effort to stand her ground, refusing to be cowed.

'Stay away from me, Kaylie—if you know what's good for you.' With that last parting shot he left her and she closed her eyes, wounded all over again by his savagery. Damn her own hide for being stupid enough to imagine even for a split second that there was still a human being beneath that arrogant shell—hadn't she learned her lesson by now? For a long moment she stood immobile, taking deep breaths in a vain bid to calm the emotions whirling so turbulently in her soul.

'Tired out already, Kaylie? Is the work proving too much for you?'

Her head jerked sharply upward at the sound of the coolly mocking voice, and she found herself looking into Claire's scornful eyes.

'I'm perfectly fine, thank you,' she returned with as much dignity as she could muster. 'Was there something you wanted me to do?'

Claire's thin lips twisted. 'If it was up to me I'd set you to work tidying up the muck-heap,' she said nastily. 'Though frankly I'm not sure you could be trusted to get even that right.'

'That's enough.' Coming so soon after Flynn's attack, the younger girl's insolence was just too much to bear. 'Frankly, Claire, I've had just about all I'm prepared to take from you—you appear to think you can get away with murder because you're related to Amanda, but that means less than nothing to me. Now—what did you want?'

The other girl shrugged, but Kaylie had seen the surprise in her eyes and mentally awarded herself a pat on the back. It was high time the worm started doing a bit of turning, she realised—she'd allowed the atmosphere in the yard to cow her for quite long enough.

'Amanda says you need a bit of light relief,' Claire said sullenly.

'Light relief?' Kaylie's grey eyes widened in amazement. 'What does that mean?'

'Amanda thinks you've been having a hard time of it recently—no more than you deserve...' Claire caught the warning look on Kaylie's face and swallowed the rest of the sentence. 'Anyway, she wants to make it up to you.' She drew one hand from behind her back and held out a riding hat. 'She thinks it's high time you were having a shot in the saddle.'

'The saddle?' Kaylie felt a ridiculous urge to laugh out loud. 'But I've only ever ridden once before in my life and I——'

'Fell off and broke your arm—yes, we know. Flynn told us.' The girl's expression was faintly disdainful. 'Amanda thinks you should try again.'

Instinctively Kaylie shook her head. 'Tell her thanks from me, but——'

'So you're chicken.'

Realising she was being taunted, Kaylie did her level best not to rise to the bait. 'No, not chicken, simply——'

'Terrified,' Claire stated blandly. 'Go on, admit it, you're scared to death. No wonder Flynn thinks you're a waste of space.'

She was being dared and she knew it—it was like being back in the school playground all over again, and any mature, level-headed person would simply refuse to play the game. But if she did refuse the dare she'd lose the minuscule amount of ground she'd gained a few moments ago by standing up to Claire. And something told her she'd never regain it. After a long moment she gave a single abrupt nod.

'Very well. If Amanda wants me to ride a horse then I will.'

Claire turned away, but not before Kaylie spotted the satisfied glint in her eyes. 'Good. Come on down to the lunging ring. We've got a horse all tacked up for you.'

Amanda was nowhere to be seen when Kaylie reached the ring, but Jan was holding two horses and handed both sets of reins to Claire with a strange look before hurrying off towards the yard.

'Here.' Claire nodded towards a finely built chestnut which looked to Kaylie's nervous eyes to be as big as the average house. 'You ride Mayfly. Amanda will be here in a minute.'

'What's she like?' Apprehension was clear in her voice, and she knew from the other girl's supercilious grin that she'd heard it too.

'Mayfly? Quiet as a lamb. Go on, you know how to get on board, don't you?'

'I'll wait for Amanda.'

Claire gave a snort of disgust. 'Don't be daft. Mayfly will only get restless if she's kept standing about.'

Uttering a silent but very heartfelt prayer, Kaylie secured the chinstrap on her hard hat, then placed one foot in the stirrup, horribly aware of a cold knot of fear settling in her stomach as she swung herself into the saddle. She tried to smile down at Claire, then gave up the effort, knowing her lips were trembling.

'Now what do I do?'

Claire rolled her eyes heavenwards. 'Just walk her round for a while,' she said with ill-concealed impatience. 'Take her into the field if you like.'

What she'd really have liked was to quit while the going was still good, while she was still in one piece. But if she did it would doubtless be reported straight back to Flynn, and she couldn't bear to see the scorn in his eyes grow still deeper. With a heavily resigned sigh she nodded.

'OK. Just make sure there's an ambulance on stand-by.'

A tiny shadow of doubt flickered in Claire's eyes, but she shook her head. 'You'll be fine.'

Desperately trying to remember what she'd been taught in her one and only riding lesson more than ten years before, Kaylie gently nudged the mare's sides with her heels, grateful when the animal obligingly began to walk forward. She'd just reached the entrance to the field when a sudden fierce yell startled her and she instinctively clutched hard on the mare's sides. The chestnut reacted as if she'd been shot, rising in a half-rear that threw Kaylie off-balance, then she touched down and took off like a bullet from a gun.

It had all happened so fast that for the first few moments Kaylie felt no fear at all as Mayfly hurtled at breakneck speed over the grass. She gripped hard on the reins, her knuckles whitening with the effort of pulling with all her strength, but the mare barely seemed to notice, her speed

lessening not at all. She was bolting, Kaylie
realised with sudden horrifying clarity—running
completely out of control—and there was absolutely nothing she could do about it. Then a strong
instinct for self-survival took over, making her
cling on like a limpet, her legs clamped vice-like
to the animal's sides.

'Kaylie! For the love of God, pull her round
in a circle!'

Flynn's voice came to her through a haze and
though her entire body felt rigid she managed to
turn her head slightly to see him astride a
powerful-looking grey. Barely even realising what
she was doing, she pulled hard on the left rein.
Mayfly arced round, leaning inward like a
motorbike, and a fresh paroxysm of terror shot
through Kaylie's veins. If the mare should over-
balance and fall to the ground at this speed, they
could both be smashed to bits.

From the corner of her eye she saw a flash of
grey and, with the tiny part of her brain that was
still functioning, realised Flynn was catching up
at her side. His hand snaked out towards
Mayfly's bridle, then she was almost catapulted
into mid-air as he leaned back, hauling both animals to a halt. Before she even had time to
understand what was happening, he'd leapt to the
ground and was beside her horse, his hands at
her waist to drag her unceremoniously from the
saddle.

'What the hell do you think you're doing?'

She looked up into his white, contorted features and all the shock and terror of the last few
minutes caved in on her. Tears welled in her eyes

and with a muffled oath he released the catch on her hard hat, pulling it from her head. Then his arms went round her, tightening convulsively, his fingers pushing deep into her hair.

'Dear God, Kaylie,' he breathed. 'I thought I'd lost you. I thought you were going to be killed.'

She tried to speak, but her voice cracked on an anguished sob and he groaned deeply, then dipped his head to find her mouth with his own in a harsh, desperate kiss. She was instantly caught up in a whirlwind of feeling, his touch driving all conscious thought from her mind, and her lips parted, begging for more of this brutal, vital invasion.

His hands ran ruthlessly over her body, sending tongues of flame where icy terror had reigned only moments before. She moved against him restlessly, aching for his touch, her own fingers digging into his back to pull him closer still. She'd lost all notion of time and place, reality disappearing in a wild whirl of sheer physical need. The only thing left to her was Flynn and the knowledge of how much she needed him.

As if he'd read her mind he suddenly froze, flinging her away from him with a force that almost sent her crashing to the ground.

'You stupid bitch!' he spat venomously, his vivid blue eyes blazing with fury. 'How dare you take a joy-ride on one of my horses?'

CHAPTER SEVEN

SHOCKED beyond belief at this sudden volte-face, she could only stare up at him, the colour draining from her already pale skin.

'I didn't! Amanda said——'

'Amanda said?' He gripped her by the shoulders, then dropped his hands abruptly as though burned by the very touch of her. 'She said what?'

'She said she wanted me to ride the horse.' In the face of his livid anger it was all she could do to stand her ground.

'You're trying to tell me she stood there and watched as you mounted Mayfly?'

'Well, no.' Kaylie closed her eyes hopelessly, knowing even before she began that he'd never listen. 'Claire came into the tack-room and told me Amanda wanted me to have a ride. When I got down to the lunging ring, Claire put me on Mayfly.'

'And you were insane enough to think you could handle her?' He nodded abruptly at the chestnut mare, his eyes narrowing as he took in her sweat-lashed skin and heaving flanks. 'This is a nervy, temperamental animal, one only an expert should ride. If Amanda was generous enough to suggest you ride something, she must have meant Tinker here.' He laid a hand on the grey horse's neck and the animal whickered softly. 'He's the schoolmaster of the stables—the one we always use to try out newcomers and rank amateurs.'

'I didn't want to ride any of the blasted horses!' Goaded by his contempt, Kaylie felt her own anger begin to push through the mass of anguish and self-doubt swirling in her brain. 'I only agreed because I couldn't stand the idea of you believing I was a coward.'

'So you decided to show off your bravery by riding one of the most valuable and difficult animals in the entire yard?' His eyes raked over her and she shrivelled inside at their look of blistering scorn. 'I can only thank God I had to return to the yard and saw what you were doing.'

'I was managing all right till you yelled at me,' she returned mutinously. 'You frightened me—and the horse.'

'I yelled at you because I could barely believe the evidence of my own eyes,' he shot back. 'Mayfly's never even been ridden in that field—she'd have taken off with you the second her hooves touched green grass, because she knew she had a total beginner on her back.' He gave a disgusted snort and handed her Tinker's reins. 'We've kept these animals out here long enough—and heaven alone knows what damage you've done to Mayfly. She's at a delicate stage in her training—you've probably set her back several weeks with your stupidity.'

'What about the damage done to me? Don't you even care about that?' The words burst from her before she could stop them.

His lips thinned to a cruel white line. 'Frankly, Kaylie, no, I don't care. If you want to play with fire you must be prepared to be burnt. Just don't risk burning anything I care for, if you value your own skin.'

He stroked one hand over the mare's neck, murmuring soothing words to her, then began leading her back towards the yard, Kaylie falling in behind with the biddable Tinker. Amanda and Claire were standing beside the lunging ring, the blonde wearing an expression of concern.

'Are you all right, Kaylie?' she asked, laying one hand on Kaylie's shoulder. 'I could hardly believe it when Claire said you'd leapt up on Mayfly.' She turned towards Flynn. 'I'm sorry, this is obviously all my fault. I did suggest she should have a ride, but I never imagined anything like this could happen.'

'Don't blame yourself,' Flynn returned shortly. 'It's not your fault that Kaylie's a fool.'

'Now wait just a minute!' Suddenly she'd taken all the insults and gibes she could stomach. 'I would never have ridden Mayfly if Claire hadn't told me to.'

Flynn and Amanda turned expectantly to Claire, who flushed very faintly beneath their scrutiny, but nevertheless managed to meet their eyes, her own expression bland.

'What possible reason could I have for doing such a thing?' she said guilelessly, and, furious as she was, Kaylie couldn't help but ruefully admire the younger woman's easy duplicity. She'd avoided telling an outright lie—and it was clear from the look on Flynn's face that he saw no reason to suspect her.

'I believe that takes care of that,' he said grimly, holding up one imperious hand when Kaylie tried to speak. 'I don't want to hear any more about it. Claire, you look after these animals—make sure Mayfly's fully calmed down before you put her back in the loose box.' He turned back to Kaylie. 'Go and get a jacket.'

'A jacket? Why?'

'Because you're coming with me. I'm not going to leave you in the yard to cause more problems.'

Even as she opened her mouth to protest, Kaylie spotted the look of annoyed surprise that flashed over Amanda's features.

'That's not necessary, Flynn,' she cut in. 'I'll be here. I'll keep an eye on Kaylie.'

He shook his head. 'You don't have time,' he returned shortly. 'She's coming with me.'

It was on the tip of her tongue to tell Flynn just where he could go, but Kaylie bit the words back. Frankly the thought of accompanying him after all that had just happened was about as appealing as spending a couple of hours alone with a hungry sabre-toothed tiger, but Amanda's anger had been very revealing. She clearly didn't want Flynn and Kaylie to spend time alone together— so maybe it would be in her best interests to swallow her pride and go along for the ride, uncomfortable though it was bound to be.

'I don't need a jacket,' she said quietly. 'I'm ready to go.'

'Very well. Have it your own way.' Amanda didn't even attempt to hide her irritation as she flounced off across the yard, Kaylie gazing after her speculatively.

'Come on, then, we haven't got time to stand around here all day. I've wasted enough time as it is.'

With a tiny sigh Kaylie followed him to the car. At one time, spending the whole day with Flynn would have been a joy; now the prospect was enough to make a dull, leaden weight settle in the pit of her stomach. Well, she'd simply have to get through the ordeal as best she could.

Under different circumstances she'd have thoroughly enjoyed the trip—the weather was glorious, with wide expanses of blue sky unmarred by cloud, and the scenery as the miles sped past ever more eye-catching. It was as well she had the beautiful countryside to concentrate on, she thought wryly, since conversation in the car was non-existent, the atmosphere frigid.

She ventured a glance towards the silent driver, her eyes riveted by the sight of his hands on the wheel, the fingers long, strong and infinitely capable. Those hands could manoeuvre a powerful car or stop a runaway horse with equal ease—but they were also capable of infinite gentleness. She'd once known that for herself— Flynn had frequently ministered to her youthful cuts and bruises, soothing away the pain with a tenderness beyond his years. Now that tenderness seemed reserved solely for his horses— and, she acknowledged with a sinking heart, for Amanda.

'Tell me about the horse we're going to see,' she said suddenly, desperate to divert her own thoughts.

'It's got four legs and a tail,' he returned curtly, never taking his eyes from the road. 'What else do you need to know?'

She bit her lip, any hope that his mood might have mellowed evaporating.

'Look, Flynn,' she tried again. 'I know what happened this morning was unforgivable, and I'm sorry, but it really wasn't——'

'It was more than unforgivable—it was insane,' he gritted out. 'And don't try telling me it wasn't your fault, Kaylie. Unless you're going to tell me Claire bodily lifted you into Mayfly's saddle?'

'Of course not, but——'

'Then you can hardly lay the blame on anyone else but yourself, can you.' It was a statement, not a question. 'And coming on top of the other ridiculous stunts you've pulled...!' He shook his head, as if finding it hard to believe any one person could be capable of so many blunders. 'If you were an employee of mine, you wouldn't have lasted two minutes in that yard. I'd have sent you packing straight away—you can't afford to have incompetent idiots around valuable and sensitive animals.'

She tried to count to ten, but the words burst from her before she'd got halfway. 'It doesn't even occur to you that I might possibly be telling the truth—that I'm the wronged and innocent party—that someone else has been responsible?'

He slid her a sideways look. 'Give me one good reason why I should believe that.'

She gave a helpless shrug. The Flynn of old would have believed her automatically before anyone else. This one seemed determined to believe the very worst of her at every turn. She couldn't win.

'All right, Flynn,' she said quietly. 'You've set your mind against me to such an extent that I've got practically no hope of convincing you of the truth. But I will. Heaven knows how, but I will.' She turned away from him then, concentrating her full attention on the scenery beyond the glass, though in reality she was seeing none of it. All she knew in that moment was a burning determination to carry out her promise, whatever it took.

'Here, lass, hold on to this big fellow for a moment, would you?'

Astonished, Kaylie automatically grabbed the reins flung haphazardly in her direction by a harassed-looking man in breeches and boots as he hurried past, muttering to himself. Even to her inexperienced eye it had been obvious straight away that the yard they were visiting wasn't nearly as well organised as Flynn's. In fact—she couldn't help but smile as she glanced around her—it was chaotic. Still, for all the hustle and bustle, the atmosphere was infinitely nicer than at Cedar Wood Stables—she'd felt the warmth and friendliness of the place wrap itself around her as soon as they'd arrived. Flynn had disappeared into the office, presumably to seek out the owner, leaving Kaylie alone and unintroduced in the yard. But before she'd had time to even gather her thoughts she'd found herself left in charge of a big rangy bay.

'All right, lad.' Managing to sound considerably more confident than she felt, she patted the animal gingerly on the shoulder. 'Just stand quiet for a moment. You'll be fine.' To her considerable relief the horse seemed perfectly content to stand at her side, nuzzling into her shoulder from time to time.

'Well, look at this—you've only been in the yard for two minutes and they've found you a job already!' A loud, jovial voice at her shoulder made her turn round, and she found herself gazing into the friendliest brown eyes she could remember seeing in a very long time. Warmed by the sight, she grinned back as though greeting a long-lost friend. At the man's side stood Flynn, his expression considerably less benign.

'What do you think you're doing, Kaylie?' he said abruptly. 'Why are you holding this horse?'

Her smile faded. 'Because someone asked me to.'

'And you're doing fine,' the other man cut in, sending Flynn a curious glance. 'Bucky can be a naughty lad, but he's settled with you.' He chuckled richly. 'Look at him nuzzling into you like that—looks like butter wouldn't melt in his mouth, doesn't he?' He nodded in satisfaction. 'Obviously recognises a sympathetic soul when he sees one.'

Immeasurably boosted by the compliment, Kaylie couldn't resist glancing at Flynn, but the shuttered look was still in his blue eyes and she sighed inwardly.

'Well, what do you think of him?' The brown-eyed man nodded questioningly towards the horse. 'Not the most handsome you've ever seen, perhaps, but loads of potential.'

Flynn smiled. 'I'll judge that for myself.'

'Of course. I'll get one of the girls to put him over the jumps for you.'

Flynn shook his head. 'I'll try him.'

The other man's jaw dropped. 'You will? Don't tell me you're finally back in the saddle?' He gave a loud guffaw and clapped Flynn heartily on the shoulder. 'Well, I couldn't be more pleased! What's brought this about?'

Flynn glanced at Kaylie, his expression wry. 'Let's just say circumstances put me back in the saddle.'

'And about time too! Come on, then—he's all yours.'

Watching Flynn ride was an experience Kaylie knew she'd never forget. She'd seen him on horseback often enough years ago, but hadn't then fully appreciated his superb skill and mastery. Now, as she stood at the side of the arena with the brown-eyed man, who had by this time introduced himself as Tom, she realised she was watching an expert, but there was more to it than that, more than just technical ability. Even though he'd never ridden Bucky before today, she could sense the bond forging itself between horse and man. He sat so still astride the big, powerful beast, controlling him with no apparent effort, almost becoming one with the horse as they soared easily over the jumps.

At her side Tom drew in his breath sharply, then grinned down at Kaylie.

'That's a sight I was afraid I'd never see again,' he said quietly. 'There's no one like Flynn Donovan on horseback—no one. He's like poetry when he rides.' He eyed her speculatively, his eyes narrowing. 'Would I be right in thinking you had something to do with this?'

She gave a rueful little smile. 'I suppose you could say that,' she admitted. 'Unfortunately he had to rescue me when a horse ran away with me.'

Tom chuckled. 'So he was playing the Sir Galahad role, was he? Well, it's done the trick, and I couldn't be happier. He's got a lot to thank you for.'

She turned away, unable to face the warm brown eyes any longer. A lot to thank her for? The cruel irony of those well-meaning words cut into her like a knife.

'I've known Flynn for a lot of years now,' Tom continued, apparently unaware of her consternation. 'He's been like a son in many ways—but since the accident it's as though he'd built a shell around himself. Wouldn't let anyone close—not even me.' He laid a warm hand on her shoulder. 'Maybe you're the one who'll finally get through that shell.'

Before she could answer, he strode away to the entrance of the arena to greet Flynn as he rode out, leaving Kaylie to gaze after him with agonised eyes. It was hard to believe that the words of a stranger could hurt so much, particularly since he'd obviously intended to be kind.

But then, she acknowledged painfully, Tom had simply voiced her own deepest wish. And it was only in hearing that wish spoken out loud that she was finally forced to accept how ludicrous it was. Flynn had nothing but contempt for her. She was the last person on earth who'd be allowed to break through that shell.

The journey home was equally silent. Flynn's mood was different, the expression on his face thoughtful rather than angry, but she was too dispirited to try drawing him out. She was nothing to him but a nuisance who had to be endured for a few more weeks, and the knowledge of that dragged on her like a heavy weight round her neck. Eventually she slipped into a light, fitful sleep, oblivious to the miles speeding past, until Flynn drew to a halt in the stable yard.

Moving slowly, she climbed out of the car and headed towards the house, intending to go straight to bed. But at the door he stopped her.

'Come and have a night-cap with me.'

Taken aback by the unexpected invitation, she glowered at him.

'Why?'

'Why?' The ghost of a smile played about his lips. 'Because I don't like drinking alone.'

'Then call Amanda. I'm sure she'd be only too glad to come rushing over.' She knew she sounded waspish, but was too tired to care.

His smile vanished. 'I'm sure she would. But I don't want to wait for her.'

'And I'm handy?' She shot him a bitter look. 'Thanks for the compliment. But frankly I don't particularly want to have a drink with you.'

'Why not?'

'Why not?' She could barely believe the question. 'You've hardly addressed more than half a dozen words to me all day, and none of those has been civil. Doubtless you've got a few more callous gibes tucked away for me—why should I hand you the opportunity to use them?'

He unlocked the door and she walked past him into the hall. Then his hand snaked out and caught her by the wrist, halting her in her tracks.

'One drink, Kaylie.'

'I've already told you,' she said through gritted teeth. 'I don't want a damned drink.'

He tugged her wrist, and the unexpected move made her stumble back against him, the touch of his warm, powerful body against her own making her tremble. Dear lord, even when she was close to hating him, she still wanted him! How could she ever hope to be free of this man's spell?

'Look,' he said quietly, 'I know I've been rough on you today. I'm sorry.'

The apology, grudged though it might have been, took the wind clean out of her sails, and it was all she could do not to give in to the urge to lean against him. A depth of will-power she hadn't even known she possessed helped her to push herself away, pulling her wrist free from his grasp.

'All right,' she said in a low voice. 'One drink.'

In the living-room she threw herself down into one of the big old armchairs as he poured a couple of generous Scotches, then handed one to her.

'I'm afraid I don't have Campari. Will this do?'

She glanced up at him in amazement, struck by the sudden suspicion that he was teasing her, ludicrous though the notion seemed. But his expression was perfectly serious and after a moment she gave a single abrupt nod.

'Whisky's fine.'

'So.' He moved to the other armchair, dropping his long frame into it with obvious pleasure. 'What did you think of Bucky?'

'What did I think of him?' The question left her nonplussed. 'Is this a trick question? I could see he had four legs and a tail—isn't that all you'd expect of me?'

His mouth twisted into a rueful grin. 'OK, I deserved that. But I'd like to know anyway.'

'I thought he was terrific,' she said guardedly. 'When you rode him over the jumps, he looked like a sure-fire winner.' She paused for a long moment, still expecting an acid rejoinder. When none came, she asked tentatively, 'Have you bought him?'

His expression changed, became withdrawn. 'No. I haven't bought him.'

'But why?'

'He cost too much.'

'I thought Tom was a friend.'

He sent her a wryly mocking look. 'He's also a businessman.'

'A dealer?'

'Of a kind.'

'Then he should know that having you ride Bucky would be a terrific advertisement.'

He eyed her thoughtfully. 'This yard hasn't produced a winner in months.'

'You haven't been riding. With you on board, Bucky could go anywhere.' She bit her lip. Now, for sure, he would pounce. Now he would tell her she didn't know the remotest thing about horses. Which of course was true. But she did know Flynn Donovan—or at least, she knew his will to succeed.

'Look,' she said quickly, 'couldn't you persuade one of your other owners to buy Bucky— or at least buy a share with you?'

He sighed heavily, passing one hand wearily over his face, and she was gripped by a sudden longing to reach out to him, to soothe away the lines of strain.

'It's not as easy as that,' he said at last. 'My other owners are waiting for signs of success before they commit anything else to me.'

'Why haven't you had that success?' A strangely detached part of her mind marvelled at her own daring in asking the question.

He shrugged his broad shoulders. 'Call it the luck of the Irish,' he said, with a flash of grim humour. 'Only in this case, it's the bad luck. Over the past six months or so, we've had a run of misfortune—horses going lame or off colour, or simply turning out like Buster, all promise and no substance.'

'So it's not just me,' she said softly. 'I'm not the jinx.'

For perhaps the first time since she'd arrived in the yard, he smiled at her, a real, genuine smile that seemed to embrace her, warming the frozen places in her soul.

'No,' he said quietly. 'You're not the jinx. But you haven't helped. You could have been killed today, Kaylie.'

'Or hurt the horse.' She took a hefty sip of the whisky, grimacing at the taste. 'I know, and I'm sorry. It won't happen again.'

He nodded, then laid his head back against the chair and closed his eyes.

'Are you hungry?' she asked. 'I could easily rustle something up in the kitchen for you.'

He shook his head. 'No, I'm not hungry. But there is something you could do.'

'What's that?'

'Give me a neck rub.' He opened his eyes and gazed directly at her and she felt a shiver start deep inside at the look in the vivid velvety blue depths. 'You used to be very good at that, as I recall.'

'Sure I won't break your neck by accident?' Her attempt at a light, casual laugh didn't quite make it and he grinned.

'I'll take the risk.'

The distance from her chair to his could only have been a few feet, but to Kaylie it seemed to yawn before her like a great, gaping chasm. Resolutely she forced herself to her feet and walked over to stand behind him, her hands trembling as she flexed her long fingers. He dipped his head forward, revealing the back of his neck, and she took a deep breath to steady the nerves chattering in her stomach, before laying her hands on his warm skin. She'd given him neck rubs hundreds of times before, she reminded herself wildly—so why was the touch of him beneath her fingers sending tiny electric shocks racing through her veins now?

'You're very tense,' she said, searching desperately for words in a mind suddenly devoid of rational thought. 'Your muscles are all knotted up.'

'Then un-knot them for me,' he murmured, easing his head from one side to the other to make the most of her ministrations. 'Dig in a bit more, girl—you never used to be so tentative.'

She began rotating the pads of her thumbs over his skin, pressing harder and harder till he groaned, then she snatched her hands away as though she'd been burned. He twisted round to look up at her, his dark blue eyes unreadable.

'What did you stop for?'

'I thought I'd hurt you.'

A slow, lazy smile curved his mouth, setting off a tremor deep within her.

'Pain like this I can take a lot of,' he said. 'And right now you're only tickling the surface.' He stood up and shrugged off his tweed jacket, throwing it carelessly on to a chair, then began unbuttoning his shirt.

'What are you doing?' Horrified, she could only stare at him in dismay.

'What does it look as though I'm doing?' he returned easily. 'You can't give me a proper neck

rub through layers of clothes, so...' He undid
the last button and peeled the shirt off, revealing
a tanned and muscular chest, lavishly covered
with silky black hair. 'I'm getting rid of the
layers. You don't mind, do you?' His eyes glinted
mockingly down at her. 'You've seen me half
naked before. For all I know, you've seen a
number of men completely naked. After all,
you're a grown woman now—not my little Kaylie
any more.'

She swallowed painfully, unable to meet his
eyes. What would he say if he knew the truth—
that it was because in her heart she was still his
that she'd never been able to give herself to any
other man? But she could never tell him—could
never reveal how much she felt for him, how
much she'd always felt for him. She couldn't bear
to see incredulous scorn, or, worse still, pity in
his velvet blue eyes.

'It doesn't matter to me,' she said at last,
aching with every lying syllable. 'And you're
right, of course, it is more practical this way. Sit
down.'

He shook his head. 'I've got a better idea.'

'You have?'

'We might as well do this properly.' He nodded
towards the flames flickering in the grate. 'Good
old Mrs Mac always insists on a fire, even on
mild nights like this. Tonight I'm glad of it.'

'Why? What are you going to do with it?' Even
to her own ears the question sounded inane and
she clenched her fists as he gave her a pained
look.

'I'm going to lie down in front of it,' he explained with exaggerated patience. 'On the sheepskin rug.'

Oh, lord, she thought wildly, could things get any worse? This was the stuff her fantasies had been made of over the long years they'd been apart, when she'd never been able to rid her mind of memories of him. Was he doing this on purpose? Was this another ploy to get her away from the yard, by driving her insane? Uttering a silent plea for strength, she gave a little nod.

'Good idea. The heat will help relax your muscles.'

He stretched out on his stomach in front of the fire, the muscles rippling in his back as he laid his head on his folded arms, and for a long moment she could only watch, hypnotised by the soft play of firelight over his shadowed skin.

'Come on, then,' he grunted impatiently. 'Get on with the job.'

She knelt awkwardly at his side, flinching when her knee touched his naked back. Summoning up every shred of will-power she possessed, she reached forward to lay her hands on his shoulders, forced to close her eyes as the warmth of his skin sent a tremor of longing right through her own body.

She moved her probing fingers over his back, desperately trying to conjure up thoughts of income tax or foggy days—anything to get her mind off what was really happening. It was no use. She might as well have plugged an erotic video into her brain.

Instead of the doom and gloom she was trying to engender, her wayward imagination seemed determined to behave like Mayfly—ignoring her restraining hands and rushing madly along its own chosen path. Without even realising she was doing it, she leaned closer into his back, his warm, male smell making her senses reel. In her mind she was wearing not jeans and a sweat-shirt, but a frothy concoction of practically nothing, so that when she straddled his back her near-naked breasts would press shamelessly into his skin as she reached down to kiss the back of his neck. He'd turn in one easy move, enfolding her in his arms and tumbling her on to the sheepskin rug, his big, powerful body covering hers. She'd feel the dense mat of hair on his chest rub against her own tender skin and he'd murmur her name in his soft Irish voice...

'Kaylie?'

She sat up abruptly, rigid with shock as the spell shattered into a million jagged pieces.

'Are you all right?' He twisted round to rest on one elbow, his eyes faintly quizzical as he stared up at her.

'I'm fine,' she stammered, striving to gather her badly scattered wits. She had just been fantasising, hadn't she? She couldn't really have...

'You've still got a sure touch.' Flynn's expression was bland. 'Almost as good as Amanda's. Thanks—I should be able to get some sleep now.'

He rose to his feet, leaving her kneeling on the floor, feeling as though a dagger had just been plunged into her heart. He'd been using her—

making her into a substitute because Amanda wasn't available. Getting her to perform a service his beautiful blonde partner usually carried out, and apparently with more skill. She could only give silent thanks that he hadn't required any other kind of service, because, heaven help her, if he'd tried, she'd have been putty in his hands.

'You're welcome.' Calling on her entire reserves of inner strength, she was able to answer without a flicker of emotion as she got to her feet. 'My male friends always tell me I've got good hands. I'm glad they were able to help you a little.' She walked past him to the door without once looking up into his eyes, knowing that could be her undoing. 'Goodnight, Flynn. Sleep well.'

CHAPTER EIGHT

'LAURA, can you spare five minutes? I want to talk to you.'

The younger woman glanced up from tack cleaning, with a friendly smile. 'Sure. What's wrong?'

Kaylie shook her head. 'Not here. I want to talk in private. Let's go up to my room.'

Laura's expression grew wary, but after a moment she nodded. 'OK.'

Upstairs, Kaylie closed the bedroom door firmly behind her, and motioned Laura to sit on the bed.

'Right,' she said firmly. 'I want to know what's going on in this yard.'

'Going on?' Laura tried to look taken aback, but lacked Claire's skill in masking her true feelings. It was clear she wasn't surprised by the question.

Kaylie nodded. 'I think you know what I'm talking about. I understand from Flynn that he's been having a run of what he prefers to call "bad luck" recently. I don't think it's as simple as that. I also don't believe you're involved—but I think you can help me get to the bottom of it all.'

Laura glanced down at the bed, unconsciously twisting the candlewick spread between her fingers. For a long moment she was silent, then she sighed heavily.

'I wasn't sure for a long time,' she said quietly. 'In fact it's only really since you've been here that I . . .' Her voice faded away.

'That you what, Laura?' Kaylie urged gently. 'Come on, what is it you're afraid of?'

The girl shook her head. 'This is a good job. I don't want to lose it.'

'And you think you might if you blow the whistle on the others?' Kaylie sat down beside her on the bed. 'That won't happen, Laura. Flynn's a fair man. He'd never sack you for telling the truth.'

'But Amanda's his partner.' Her voice was so low as to be barely audible.

Kaylie drew her breath in sharply. 'So Amanda's behind things?' Laura remained silent, her fingers twisting the coverlet still more frantically. Kaylie put a hand on her shoulder. 'Come on,' she said softly, 'you've started now; you must go on. What's happened since I've been here to make you suspicious?'

Laura took a deep breath. 'Well,' she began slowly, 'I didn't think too much about it when you nearly gave Julius sugar-beet instead of pony nuts. That could have been a genuine mistake—after all, no one could really expect you to know the difference.' She frowned, remembering the incident. 'Though I did think at the time that Claire should have been a bit more vigilant—she certainly knows the dangers of unsoaked sugar-beet.' She waved one hand in a dismissive gesture. 'Anyway—I did start to get suspicious when I heard about the tangled tack.'

'Why?' Kaylie's eyes were riveted to Laura's face.

'Because I personally checked the work you'd done after you left the tack-room that afternoon.' She smiled faintly. 'I know from my own experience how easy it is to get bridles in a muddle if you've taken them to bits before cleaning them. I didn't want you to get into any more trouble, so I was going to sort things out if necessary.'

Kaylie squeezed her arm gratefully, and was about to speak, but Laura glanced up into her eyes.

'It wasn't necessary,' she said slowly, almost spelling out the words. 'You'd put everything back together perfectly.'

Kaylie sat back with a thump, washed by a wave of relief. 'I knew it!' she said. 'I knew I couldn't have been so stupid.'

'I didn't say anything about it at the time, because I didn't want to get involved if I could avoid it. But yesterday was the last straw,' Laura continued. 'I know you're nervous round the horses, and I know you'd never have chosen of your own free will to ride Mayfly. Anyone could tell just from looking at her that she's a hothead. But, frankly, even if you'd been dead-set determined to ride her, Claire should have done whatever it took to keep you off her back.'

'You're saying Claire set me up?'

Laura nodded slowly and with obvious reluctance.

'But why?' Kaylie frowned. 'I can't think of any good reason for it at all.'

'Maybe she and Amanda are afraid of you discovering the other things going on round the yard—maybe they've been trying to make you so unhappy that you'll leave of your own accord.'

Kaylie gazed at her steadily, sensing the girl's remaining uncertainty. If she made a wrong move now, Laura could still close up like a clam, and she'd be left none the wiser.

'What "other things"?' she said gently. 'Come on, Laura, you've come this far already—you must tell me the rest.'

Laura closed her eyes tightly, as if gathering courage; then she looked directly at Kaylie.

'Something's going on behind Flynn's back,' she said, her words coming out in a rush. 'Something that could hurt him.'

'Does it involve Buster?' Kaylie hazarded, remembering Flynn's anxiety about the big horse.

'Buster, and several others before him who promised a lot, but at the end of the day delivered nothing. Flynn's reputation has suffered a lot because of it. If his luck doesn't change soon, he's in danger of being wiped out completely. People won't send their horses to a yard that isn't winning.'

'Then why hasn't he seen for himself that something's going on?' Kaylie queried. 'Flynn's far from stupid—he must realise——'

'He always blames himself,' Laura cut in. 'He's so involved with the animals that he takes it upon himself when things go wrong. But——' she paused significantly '—he's not always here.'

Kaylie laid her hand on Laura's arm, her eyes beseeching as she gazed into the younger woman's face.

'Do you know exactly what's happening?' she said urgently.

Laura shook her head. 'I only wish I did. All I have is a bad feeling, and nothing concrete to back it up with. But the others know I'm completely loyal to Flynn—they wouldn't let me in on any secrets.'

Something niggled at the back of Kaylie's mind and she screwed up her eyes in fierce concentration, trying to trap the elusive thought.

'Buster's legs!' she said suddenly. 'I was in the stable with Flynn the other night when he discovered some healed-over cuts on his front legs. Could that have anything to do with all of this?'

Laura frowned. 'I don't know. What did Flynn say?'

'That someone must have been jumping him carelessly, round the cross-country jumps, perhaps.'

'Or he could have been rapped.'

'Rapped?' Kaylie frowned, not understanding the term.

Laura nodded. 'I've never had much to do with Buster—as you'll have realised, we each have our particular charges to look after. Buster is very much Claire's domain. Come to think of it, I haven't even seen him being jumped very often. Amanda tends to work him in the mornings, when I'm riding some of the others out.'

'And Flynn's tied up with other things?' Kaylie guessed.

'Very often, yes.'

'But what is rapping?'

Laura's eyes narrowed. 'It's a nasty little trick designed to make horses jump higher, because they're afraid not to. Basically the top pole of the jump is lifted just as the horse is going over, so he gets a smart rap on the legs. Next time he goes over, he'll try harder. Flynn's always forbidden the practice in this yard—says he doesn't want to train his animals through pain.'

'Could that explain Buster's lack of sparkle?'

'It could. Some animals would cope all right with it—but he's a sensitive soul.' She hesitated. 'And there could be more.'

'More?'

'If Amanda's resorted to rapping, she could also be trying out a few more dirty tricks.'

'Such as?'

'Such as putting burrs or even drawing-pins in the tendon boots—that would increase the pain when he hit the pole.'

Kaylie absorbed what she'd been told in silence. 'Why would Amanda be doing these things?' she said at last.

Laura shrugged. 'Who knows?'

'We have to tell Flynn,' Kaylie said decisively, but Laura shook her head.

'Don't you think I'd have told him already if I had any proof? Suspicion's not enough.'

Kaylie set her lips in a grimly determined line. 'Then we'll find proof. Whatever it takes, we'll do it. OK?'

The other girl smiled. 'OK.'

*   *   *

Over the next few days Kaylie all but glued herself to Laura's side, determined not to inadvertently fall foul of any more dirty tricks. But if she kept her head down, she kept her eyes wide open, watching at every turn for something, some tiny clue that might just give the conspirators away. She was convinced they were bound to make a slip sooner or later—if for no other reason than that they both believed her too ignorant of horses and the yard routine to notice anything out of the ordinary. The snag was, she acknowledged gloomily, they were probably right. Still, now she had Laura's eagle eyes and experience to depend on.

With Flynn she seemed to have achieved an unspoken and uneasy truce—the blatant hostility had gone from his eyes when he glanced in her direction, replaced by a kind of wry watchfulness which in its way was almost as hard to accept since it proved he still didn't have much faith in her abilities, but at least didn't cut her to ribbons inside as his contempt had. She ruthlessly shoved thoughts of the neck rub episode to the back of her mind, knowing that to dwell on it could only bring more pain. What she needed right now was strength.

To her delight, he'd started riding regularly again. Amanda wasn't so pleased. She couldn't mask her displeasure when she saw Flynn schooling Buster in the paddock, her eyes narrowing dangerously as she turned on Kaylie.

'I suppose this is your doing,' she hissed.

'I don't think so.' Kaylie blinked, taken aback by the other woman's sudden hostility. Amanda had become adept at masking her true feelings towards Kaylie—this was the first time in days she'd let the mask slip. 'Flynn's his own man. He makes his own decisions.'

Amanda nodded grimly. 'Then I hope he hasn't made the wrong one this time,' she said shortly.

'Why should he have?' Kaylie swallowed the urge to bite back, determined to play the game of the innocent abroad to the hilt. It might be the only way to make Amanda show her hand. But the blonde merely gave a shrug.

'He hasn't ridden properly for a long time. He could do more harm than good—to himself and the horse. I'd rather have seen him ride Julius or Tinker—they're both steady enough to cope with a rider's nerves.'

Kaylie gazed at her guilelessly. 'I don't imagine he'll be unduly affected by nerves,' she said calmly. 'He's a superb horseman.'

Something flashed in Amanda's eyes, but when she turned to Kaylie her expression was bland, giving nothing away.

'Even the very best riders can overestimate their own skills,' she said evenly in a voice that nevertheless made Kaylie's skin crawl. 'Flynn's had a long lay-off. I just don't want to see him having any more accidents, that's all.'

She turned on her heels and strode off towards the stables, leaving Kaylie staring after her with a distinctly uncomfortable feeling inside. She wouldn't do anything to hurt Flynn—would she? Then she shook herself, trying to get rid of the feeling. She was becoming paranoid. Amanda and Claire might be scheming to ruin his chances of success, though for the life of her she still couldn't work out why—but surely neither of them would ever want to physically harm him? It was a ridiculous idea.

That afternoon Flynn collared her as she was about to return to the house.

'Where do you think you're going?'

'Well, I was just about to——'

'No, you aren't. You're going for a ride.'

She looked at him in blank astonishment. 'A ride?'

'Correct.'

'On a horse?'

'We don't have any cows, so I suppose it will have to be.'

She swallowed hard on a sudden debilitating rush of nerves. 'But after what happened last time——'

'It's because of what happened last time that you're going out now.' Flynn's voice was calm, yet underlaid with steel. It was clear he wouldn't take no for an answer. 'If you're nervous round the horses, they'll sense it. A few lessons should boost your confidence.'

Kaylie searched desperately in her mind for a good reason to refuse, then gave a little shrug of defeat. She'd never been a match for Flynn in fully determined mood, and it seemed that that at least hadn't changed. 'OK. If you're sure.'

'I am. Go and fetch a hard hat.'

It was to be the first of several lessons over the next few days. On her first ride Kaylie was stiff with anxiety, convinced that even the placid, biddable Tinker would take off like a rocket if she did the slightest thing wrong. But to her surprise, Flynn turned out to be a good teacher, calm and unflappable, and she began to relax, then to her amazement found she was actually enjoying herself.

'You're doing all right,' he said at the end of one session. 'Now that you're not so tense, you've got a nice, natural rhythm. You've mastered the basics—tomorrow we'll speed things up a little.'

'Can't we just stick with the slow stuff?'

He gave her a pained look. 'Where's your spirit of adventure, girl? By the time you leave here I intend to have you jumping logs and ditches.'

'Oh, God.' Kaylie rolled her eyes heavenwards as though seeking divine intervention. 'In that case I'll go and pack now.'

But she knew she wouldn't carry out the threat. Apprehensive of the horses though she still might be, she'd come to treasure the short lessons with Flynn. During those times he was closer to the Flynn of old than at any other time, though that carried a pain all of its own, making her more aware than ever of just how much he still meant to her.

She'd finally managed to unearth her beloved camera, taking shot after shot round the stables, and, when she thought she wouldn't be spotted, of Flynn on horseback. It was a sight she never ceased to be enthralled by. The day she saw him schooling Buster over jumps, the breath caught in her throat and she was forced to blink away tears. The horse too seemed to have found fresh heart, soaring over the coloured poles as though he had wings, his ears pricked in obvious enjoyment.

'Buster seems to have got over his bad patch,' she commented at lunch that day. 'It's terrific to see him looking so keen.'

Amanda's lips tightened imperceptibly. 'Too early to judge,' she said abruptly. 'That animal's got a long way to go in his training.'

'I disagree,' Flynn said evenly. 'In fact I'm seriously considering entering him for a show this weekend.'

Amanda all but choked on a mouthful of food. 'You can't be serious!'

'Why not?' Flynn eyed her curiously and Kaylie laid down her fork, riveted by the exchange.

'Because he's not ready. You could set him back if you push him too far too fast.'

'I'll be the judge of that,' Flynn returned with quiet authority. 'If I say he's ready then he's ready.'

Two spots of vivid colour flared in Amanda's pale cheeks. 'Then you can find yourself another jockey,' she said angrily. 'Because I won't ride him.'

Flynn's expression was unreadable. 'I already have a jockey,' he said. 'Myself.'

'You?' Amanda's eyes widened in shock. 'Are you crazy? You've only just started riding again. You're not ready, any more than Buster is.'

Flynn's dark brows drew together thunderously, but the threatened explosion never came. Instead he contented himself with a mild, 'We'll see.'

Amanda threw up her hands in resignation. 'If you're so dead-set determined on this mad-fool scheme, I'd better get down to some serious work with Buster, then,' she said.

Kaylie felt a twist of acid deep inside. 'Shouldn't Flynn do the work?' she ventured, almost biting her tongue out as Amanda threw her a cold, narrow-eyed glance. Damn, she had to be careful not to alert the other woman that she was being watched. Schooling her own features carefully, she gave a little shrug. 'I just mean it would seem sensible if he's to be riding Buster in the show.'

Flynn nodded. 'Yes, it would. But I'm going to be pretty tied up between now and then.'

'Really, Kaylie, I don't think you need concern yourself about what happens here in the yard,' Amanda cut in smoothly. 'I believe I'm capable of schooling Buster.'

Kaylie turned away, just in time to see a look flash between Amanda and Claire, and the feeling of apprehension within her strengthened. She'd need to be extra vigilant, she realised, since it appeared that Flynn, without knowing it, was pushing Amanda's hand. If she really was trying to discredit the yard, it would do her cause no good at all to have Flynn and Buster acquit themselves well at the show.

That afternoon Laura invited her to go out for a ride, since Flynn had an appointment in Perth, but Kaylie declined.

'Oh, come on,' Laura teased. 'I know I haven't got the master's touch, but I can still give you a few tips.'

Kaylie shook her head. 'It isn't that. But I'd like to keep a watchful eye round here while Flynn's away from base.'

Laura nodded. 'You could be right. Still, it might be to your benefit if Amanda and Claire believe you've come out with me. They'll think the coast's completely clear.'

Kaylie considered that. 'So I could cut back to the yard and spy on them?'

'Exactly. You'll need to return on foot to be less noticeable, but I know all the short cuts.'

The plan worked like a dream. Flynn went off to his appointment and a short while later Kaylie and Laura rode out of the yard together. As they reached the start of a forest trail, Laura reined in, bringing her mount to a halt.

'Right,' she said, 'follow that track and it'll bring you out behind the house. If you're careful you'll get upstairs without being spotted—go into Flynn's room and you'll have a good view of the exercise arena.' A faint frown creased her eyes. 'Just be careful, Kaylie. I don't want you landing in any trouble.'

Kaylie grinned and gave the thumbs up. 'Don't worry. I'll be careful.'

She sped back to the house, stopping to collect her camera before heading towards Flynn's room, which was in a different wing of the rambling old building. She tentatively pushed the door open, her heart in her mouth even though she knew he couldn't possibly be there, then stopped dead in her tracks as it came home to her just where she was. This was Flynn's room—his private place, his sanctuary from the world.

Her eyes were drawn irresistibly to the king-size bed. That was where he slept, where he laid his head on the pillow every night. Almost without realising she was doing it, she crossed the room and sat on the bed, absent-mindedly running her fingers over the soft cotton of the duvet cover. She could feel his presence all about her and the feeling was both warming and deeply disturbing.

She gazed with bleak eyes at the bed—had he lain with Amanda there? The foolishness of the question made her give a hollow little laugh, even as she was gripped by an acid spasm of jealousy. He was a stunningly attractive man, Amanda a beautiful woman; they worked closely together every single day. It was inevitable that their relationship would have gone beyond a simple business partnership. How would he react if she told him his glamorous partner was scheming against him? If he was in love with Amanda, he might refuse to believe a word against her—and, even if he did, his resulting bitterness might make him turn completely against Kaylie.

For long moments she simply sat there on the bed, gripped by an agonising mixture of emotions—was she really doing this for the sake of the old friendship, or was the truth really that the thought of Flynn and Amanda together ripped her apart inside?

Then she gave a tiny shrug. She had no choice. Whatever her real motive, she had to see this thing through. She owed it to Emma, and to all that Flynn had once been to her, even if at the end of the day she saw only hatred in his blue eyes.

With a resigned sigh she got to her feet, but as she was walking over to the window an open magazine on the bedside table caught her eye and she glanced down at it. To her utter amazement, she saw her own face staring back from one of the photographs on the page. With a soft exclamation she picked the magazine up to study it more closely, for a moment unable even to recognise the setting of the photo. In it, she was surrounded by a group of people, all dressed in stylish party clothes. The caption underneath read: 'The Cream Of Edinburgh Society Hitting The High Spots'.

A faint smile touched her lips as she recalled the occasion—it had been several months ago, when she'd been commissioned to take shots of a city night-club for an advertising spread. The owners had asked her to dress up for the occasion so she'd be able to mingle with the crowd more easily. Unable to muster anything sufficiently classy from her own wardrobe, she'd had to borrow an evening dress from Beth. That same evening, she remembered now, another photographer had been taking pictures for a magazine article—and it seemed, quite by chance, she'd ended up on the other end of the camera lens. Could this be the explanation behind Flynn's misguided but enduring belief that she was a regular member of the city jet-set?

A faint noise from outside caught her attention and she laid the magazine back on the table. Right now she had more important things to do than look at pictures. She moved to the window, then gave a soft exclamation of triumph as she reached quickly for her camera. Amanda was riding Buster and the horse was clearly unhappy, his ears laid right back against his head as she cantered him round. In the middle of the paddock, Claire and Jan were standing at either end of a jump, holding a long, coloured pole between them.

Kaylie quickly set the camera to motor-drive and started shooting, just as Amanda was turning into the jump. Buster gathered himself up, and as he soared over the two girls lifted the pole, catching him neatly on the legs.

'Eureka!' Kaylie muttered softly. 'Now go on, ladies, do it again—just to make sure.'

Her wish was granted, though she sent a silent apology to the unhappy Buster. In the long run he'd benefit too, even though he was clearly suffering right now. She noticed he was wearing tendon boots—either Amanda was trying to prevent any visible marks from appearing on his legs, or Laura was right and his tormentors had added a few extra nasty touches. Either way, the film in this camera should hold the proof she needed to convince Flynn that his partner wasn't all she seemed. With a tiny smile of triumph she left his room and headed back towards the other wing of the house.

The following morning she took the film to the tiny chemist shop in the nearby village, wishing for the first time since she'd left the city that she was still in Edinburgh. The film could have been

developed in an hour there, instead of the several
days that was the best the shopkeeper could
promise.

Back at the yard Flynn was schooling Mayfly
in the paddock, but for once even his authority
seemed to be failing him as the mare danced skit-
tishly about, ignoring his commands.

'What's wrong with her?' Kaylie perched on
the top rail of the fencing to watch.

'The weather,' Flynn returned shortly, swearing
under his breath as he fought to control the
prancing animal. 'There's a storm brewing, and
Mayfly knows it.'

'A storm?' Kaylie glanced apprehensively upwards, seeing for the first time the darkening
clouds overhead. 'You mean thunder and
lightning?'

Finally managing to bring the mare to a relatively settled walk, Flynn glanced over in Kaylie's
direction, his expression faintly amused.

'You never did like storms, did you? As I recall
you used to hide away in Emma's wardrobe—or
mine.'

Kaylie's cheeks flamed at the memory, but she
tossed her head loftily.

'That was a long time ago,' she said haughtily.
'I've changed since then.'

'Unfortunately not for the better.' He trotted
Mayfly over to the fence and halted just a few
feet away. 'I liked you a lot better as that little
girl.'

She flinched as though he'd slapped her, the
sudden and unprovoked attack taking her completely by surprise.

'That little girl liked you too,' she said quietly. 'Thank God she's not around any longer to see the cold, arrogant swine you've turned into.'

'*Touché*.' His blue eyes bored into her. 'But why isn't she around any longer? Because you've swamped her sweet spirit with all the dross of the city—you've extinguished the flame that was in her with too much easy living. Fast cars and fast friends—and all the things that go with them. Those things would never have suited the Kaylie I once knew—the one who'd rather have gone for a walk by my side than frequented the fanciest of night-clubs with the pick of the city's eligible playboys.' His lips curled in disgust. 'I wish to God Emma had never made that damn foolish will—I wish I'd never had to see for myself what happens when innocence is corrupted. It leaves an odour in the nostrils, Kaylie—a rank, terrible odour like decayed roses. And I smell that odour every time I look into your devious, lying eyes.'

She wanted to fight back, wanted to defend herself against the terrible stinging arrows of his unjust tongue—to tell him the truth about the photograph he'd seen. But she couldn't tell him she'd seen the magazine article in his room without explaining why she'd been there. And she couldn't do that without the developed roll of film to back up her story. In this mood he'd probably refuse to listen to a word she said.

Stabbed to the heart by his cruelty, she could only watch in silence as he swung easily out of the saddle and began leading the horse back towards the stable block. She'd really begun to believe there had been a thaw in the cold war between them—how could she have been so stupid? It looked now as if things were worse than ever.

'In the bad books again, are we?'

She turned with a feeling of cold inevitability to see Claire standing a few paces away. From her expression of smug superiority it was obvious she'd heard everything and for a fleeting second Kaylie felt a wave of hatred for Flynn. How could he say those things when someone else was in earshot?

'Did you want something?' With an effort she managed to school her voice to sound bored.

'Only to find out if there's any danger of you actually doing any work around here, or if you're intending to skive off all day,' the other girl shot back with a flash of annoyance. 'We all want to get finished early.'

'Oh, really? Why?'

'Don't you know?' A malicious glint appeared in Claire's eyes. 'It's the Charity Ball tonight. We're all going. Don't tell me you haven't been invited, Cinderella?' She pretended to look surprised, then gave a little nod. 'But then of course there isn't a partner for you, is there? Not since Flynn's taking Amanda.'

The dagger went straight in just as it had been intended to, and she had to take a deep, steadying breath before replying.

'No, I hadn't realised you were all going to a ball. Does that mean the yard will be left completely unattended?'

Claire shook her head, clearly enjoying herself. 'Apparently not. You'll be here. Unless your fairy godmother appears, complete with wand, of course, and that seems pretty unlikely. Just do your best to make sure you don't completely destroy the place in Flynn's absence.'

There and then she could happily have let the whole yard go to hang, but she'd promised to lend Laura her car that evening, so she was stuck. A veritable Cinderella indeed.

She ate dinner alone that evening, the others having gone home to prepare for the ball, and she toyed moodily with the heaped plateful Mrs Mac had left, her appetite non-existent. It wasn't that she'd have wanted to go the ball, she mused desultorily—but it would have been nice to be asked.

A self-mocking smile played about her lips—who was she trying to kid? The ball was apparently a dressy, glamorous affair, and no doubt Amanda would go to all lengths to ensure she was the belle. But it wasn't that which was sending jealousy flowing like acid through her veins—it was the thought of Flynn holding her in his arms on the dance-floor. In her mind's eye she could visualise the scene—Flynn, tall and magnificent in black dinner-jacket and starched white shirt, his blue eyes more vivid than ever as they gazed down with undisguised admiration and desire at his beautiful, curvaceous partner, her shapely form dressed to perfection in a figure-hugging sheath of silk.

With a little moan, Kaylie pushed her untouched plate away and stood up, moving restlessly towards the window. Outside the storm was beginning to gather force, rain lashing relentlessly against the glass, the wind howling mournfully through the trees. That was all she needed. She'd always been terrified of storms, ever since the train carrying her parents and brother had crashed into a tree felled by lightning. Even now the elements in filthy temper like this made her shudder, and unconsciously she wrapped her arms about herself as though to offer some comfort.

'Don't stand there and watch if it makes you uneasy.'

She turned at the sound of Flynn's voice, but any response she might have made died stillborn on her lips. She'd known he would look good in evening dress, but her imagination hadn't begun to do justice to the real thing. He was spectacular—a pagan deity clothed in the apparel of the supposedly sophisticated.

His eyes narrowed as she stared at him, unable to say a word.

'You look as if you've seen a ghost.'

She shook her head with a bleak little smile. It wasn't a ghost she'd seen, but a sudden vision of the future—a future in which Flynn would play no part, because once the conditions of Emma's will had been fulfilled there would be no reason for them ever to meet again. After all the heartache of the past few days it was a vision she should have welcomed. Instead it made her die a little inside. However savage the pain he caused, this man would always be in her soul, too deeply ingrained ever to erase. Yet here he was standing before her, looking more devastating than any mortal man had the right to—and all for another woman.

'You surprised me,' she managed at last. 'I was deep in thought when you came in.'

'Will you be all right left here by yourself?' He seemed to ask the question unwillingly.

She tilted her chin a little in unconscious defiance, her pride refusing to let him see how she really felt.

'Of course. I have the dogs for company.'

He gave a single abrupt nod. 'Fine. If you do need me for anything, the phone number of the hotel is on my desk.'

If I do need you for anything! She felt an insane desire to laugh hysterically—what on earth could she possibly need him for? Except perhaps to make her life worth living.

She sauntered across the room and flung herself casually into an armchair, reaching for a magazine.

'Try not to make too much noise when you come in,' she said with a thoroughly fake air of insouciance.

He gave an angry, indecipherable exclamation and turned away, his bad leg dragging slightly as he left the room. Left alone, she gazed at the magazine steadfastly, determined to appear engrossed if he should re-enter the room. When she heard the front door slam a few moments later she threw the magazine aside, dropping her face into her hands as the dam finally burst and tears flooded her eyes, spilling unstoppably down her cheeks.

CHAPTER NINE

FOR a long while she lay in the chair, emotionally drained by the flood of tears, too dispirited to move. Then a sudden crack of thunder startled her back to reality and she sat up abruptly, her heart racing. Her first instinct was to dive for the nearest wardrobe, then she remembered the horses stabled outside and groaned wildly. For all she knew, they might be even more frightened than she was.

'Damn you, Flynn!' she cried to the empty room. 'Why aren't you here where you're needed, instead of enjoying yourself at that blasted ball?'

For a second she did battle with her conscience, telling herself there really wasn't much she could do even if the animals were alarmed. It was no good. She couldn't just sit there in relative comfort, not knowing if they were all right or not. Muttering savagely under her breath, she grabbed a jacket from the hall, pushed her feet into a pair of boots and headed out into the night, dropping her face forward as stinging rain lashed her skin, taking her breath away.

In the stable yard the horses seemed a little restless, but otherwise fine, as she dashed from one box to the next, murmuring soothing words. But at the last box she stopped dead, her heart thudding into her stomach as she saw Buster. The animal was clearly in distress, his large, liquid eyes anxious as he glanced uneasily round at his own sides, and she could see patches of sweat glistening on his silken skin.

'What's wrong, lad?' She laid a gentle hand on his neck and he swung his head round to look at her, uttering a low, unhappy whicker. It was clear the horse was sick—perhaps a relatively minor ailment, but there was no way she could take the risk of assuming the best. She'd have to get Flynn.

Giving Buster a last reassuring pat, she hurried back to the house, shuddering as lightning streaked the sky, followed seconds later by a growl of thunder. But when she picked up the telephone in the hall, her heart fell right to the soles of her boots. The line was dead, probably a victim of the storm. And Laura had her car! She was stuck here, completely isolated, with no means of getting through to Flynn.

She braced her hands against the telephone table, taking deep breaths in a bid to steady the sudden rush of terror flooding her entire body. She'd never felt more alone or more frightened in her entire life.

'Dear God,' she breathed, 'what am I supposed to do?'

But even as she asked the question, she knew there was only one answer. The hotel was only a couple of miles away, but too far to walk when every second could be crucial. She'd have to ride there. She'd have to go back out into the storm, saddle up one of the horses, and ride through that wild dark night to Flynn. If she didn't, Buster could die.

She wasted another couple of valuable seconds marshalling every ounce of courage, fighting the insidious inner voice which kept telling her the animal probably wasn't so very sick at all, and that Flynn would be furious beyond measure to discover she'd taken one of his precious animals on such a crazy errand.

In the end, knowing she had no choice, she darted out into the night, swiftly collecting saddle, bridle and a hard hat from the tack room, before heading for Tinker's stable. The grey gelding gave her a curious look when she walked in, but stood quietly as she tacked up, her fingers turning to thumbs as she wrestled with the girth buckles.

'Now look, my beautiful boy,' she murmured as she led him into the yard, 'you've always been good to me, even though we both know I'm a hopeless amateur. Please don't let me down now!'

She swung herself into the saddle, shuddering as her seat touched the already wet saddle. The wind was howling so loudly that she could barely even hear the sound of Tinker's hooves as they made their way out of the yard. Within seconds she was soaked to the skin, her lightweight anorak no protection against the stinging needles of rain. The worst thing was the unrelenting blackness of the night, relieved only by occasional flashes of lightning. But if Kaylie was frankly terrified, Tinker seemed totally unperturbed as he picked his way sure-footedly through the puddles.

Reaching the road, he found his own way to the grass verge, and began to trot, the un-expected change of pace catching Kaylie by surprise and making her clutch instinctively at the reins.

'Don't tug on the reins, Kaylie. Horses have sensitive mouths—that's one of the first ways to upset even the quiet ones.'

She looked around wildly, hearing Flynn's calm, authoritative tones so clearly it seemed he must have suddenly materialised out of the darkness. Then she gave a nervous little laugh.

'Lord, Tinker, I must really be cracking up! I'm hearing voices now. Well, if it helps me get to the hotel, I don't mind.'

The animal's ears flicked back as he listened to her voice, then he seemed to move up a gear, his bouncy trot lengthening into a canter. Kaylie's heart leapt into her throat and lodged there, making breathing a forgotten luxury.

It was a ride that would remain engraved on her memory forever. Holding the thought of Flynn like a talisman in her mind, she was amazed to find her terror slowly evaporating, to be replaced by a strange kind of exhilaration, a tingling in her blood that was like nothing she'd ever experienced before.

Even so, when the lights of the village finally came into view she heaved a great sigh of relief, slowing Tinker to a walk as she turned into the hotel car park. She slid down from the saddle and flung the reins at a bemused-looking attendant, before rushing up the front steps and into the foyer.

'Excuse me, miss?'

She whirled round, only to catch sight of her own reflection in a full-length mirror. The sight might have made her laugh if the situation hadn't been so desperate. She looked like a scarecrow that had been left out in a storm, hair plastered about her mud-spattered face, her anorak dripping pools of water on to the carpet. Little wonder the receptionist had sounded a little taken aback.

'Can I help you? We do have a private function on here tonight.'

To which rain-sodden scruffs are most definitely not invited, Kaylie mentally tacked on with a wry flash of her old irrepressible humour.

'Yes, I know.' She turned to the grey-haired gentleman behind the front desk with her most appealing smile. 'I have to speak with one of the guests—it's absolutely imperative.'

He seemed to hesitate, his expression distinctly dubious as he cast a glance over her.

'Oh, please!' Suddenly terrified she could be thwarted even now, Kaylie gazed at him beseechingly. 'I have to find Flynn Donovan. One of his horses is sick.'

'One of Flynn's horses?' The words seemed to galvanise him into life. 'Why didn't you say so in the first place? You wait here, young lady— I'll find him for you.'

He disappeared along a corridor, reappearing seconds later with Flynn.

'What is it, Kaylie? What's happened?'

'It's Buster,' she said. 'He's sick, Flynn.'

He gave a single abrupt nod, then turned to the grey-haired man.

'John, we need Harry Loomis. Can you find him in that scrum, please, and ask him to get over to my place right away?'

Kaylie felt the sting of foolishly grateful tears in her eyes. He'd believed her. He'd trusted her enough not to waste time in questions.

'Come on, Kaylie.' He grabbed her arm and began walking towards the front door. 'We'll take my car. Harry will be right behind us.'

'But I've got Tinker outside.' She was practically forced to run to keep up with him, his bad leg not hampering his speed at all.

He stopped dead in his tracks. 'You've got what?' He spotted the hard hat in her hand, seeming to notice her bedraggled appearance for the first time. 'Are you telling me you rode here? Through the storm?'

She nodded apprehensively, waiting for the explosion. Instead he gazed down at her in incredulous silence for a few endless seconds, then shook his head.

'You'll have to tell me later. Right now we have to get home to Buster. And don't worry about Tinker—there are stables here at the hotel. They'll look after him for the night.'

Back at the yard he screeched to a halt and jumped from the car, Kaylie following on behind, still a little dazed by the breakneck speed of the journey.

'What do you think?' Buster looked much the same as when she'd left, and she was torn between hoping against hope that she'd been mistaken all along, and fear of what Flynn would say if she had been.

'Colic,' he returned tersely. 'Get some more straw in here. He needs a deep bed in case he tries to roll.'

Her own pulse racing, Kaylie ran to do his bidding. She had absolutely no idea how serious colic was, but, judging by the look on Flynn's face, it was no trivial complaint. By the time she returned, another man was in the stable, shrugging off an elegant black dinner-jacket and tossing it carefully over the stable door before rolling up the sleeves of his snowy-white shirt.

'Spread that straw about, and then disappear, Kaylie,' Flynn said curtly. 'The last thing Buster needs right now is an audience.'

Kaylie flinched as though he'd physically struck her. After all she'd gone through to fetch him home, she could hardly believe he could dismiss her so brutally.

'I was just about to leave in any case,' she said, with as much dignity as she could muster. 'I realise there's nothing I can do.'

Back in the house she wandered restlessly about the kitchen, absent-mindedly preparing coffee, but forgetting to drink it as she gazed out of the window into the dark night, wondering what was happening out in the stable. She lost track of time as she stood there, immersed in thought, until the sound of the kitchen door opening behind her made her jump.

'I think he'll be OK.' The vet crossed the room to the sink to wash his hands. 'I've told Flynn I'll come back in the morning to check him.'

She nodded. 'I'm glad.'

'Flynn asked if you'd take out a blanket and a change of clothes for him. He's determined to sit vigil for the rest of the night.' He reached for a towel, his eyes regarding her consideringly. 'He's worried about the horse; that's why he was so abrupt with you.'

She felt her cheeks begin to burn and turned away, angry with her own inability to hide her feelings.

'It doesn't matter,' she said.

He laid a gentle hand on her shoulder. 'I think it does,' he said quietly. 'But Flynn's always like a bear with a sore head if any of the animals are sick.'

She managed to smile ruefully. 'Where I'm concerned, he's like a bear with a sore head full stop.' Then she bit her lip, wondering what on earth had made her say such a thing to a total stranger.

The vet chuckled. 'He should be grateful to you for what you've done tonight. Don't you let him forget it.'

She waited long enough to see him out, then ran up to Flynn's room to collect the clothes he'd asked for. Outside the storm was still continuing, but its anger was spent, and she barely noticed the distant rumbles of thunder as she sped across the yard to the stable. Flynn was in the empty loose box next door to Buster's and he took the bundle from her with a nod of thanks.

'I'll make up a bed of sorts here,' he said. 'That way I'll be close enough to keep an eye on him, but I won't disturb him.'

She turned to walk away, but his hand shot out, catching her by the wrist.

'Stay a while.'

She turned back, her expression incredulous. 'Stay?' she echoed. 'Why?'

He smiled faintly. 'Maybe I need the company right now.'

'And there's no one else around, so I'll have to do?' She shook her head bitterly. 'You didn't want me around earlier on. Don't start thinking you can simply use me whenever you feel like it.'

To her annoyance, his lips twitched in amusement. 'Still sulking because I told you to go away? Don't you think that's rather childish, Kaylie?'

Unconsciously she clenched her hands into fists as she glared back at him.

'I don't believe it's in the least bit childish to expect good manners,' she bit out. 'But you don't seem to possess any at all.'

He leaned back against the stable door, folding his arms as he regarded her consideringly. 'And what sort of good manners did you have in mind?' he drawled, his southern Irish accent more pronounced than ever. 'The kind you'd find in your fancy city night-clubs and restaurants?' His eyes hardened. 'If those surface, superficial things are all that matter to you, then heaven help you.'

She shook her head wonderingly. 'You think you know me so well,' she said. 'But you don't know me at all. You've made up your mind on the basis of entirely spurious evidence.'

'Have I, now?' The blue eyes were un-wavering. 'And just what would that be?'

She bit her lip, realising almost too late just how close she'd come to blurting out that she'd seen the magazine in his room. Even now the temptation to put him straight was all but over-whelming. But she was still determined to have the damning photographs in her hand before she told him the rest.

'It doesn't matter,' she muttered at last.

'You are right about one thing,' he said. 'I should have had good manners enough to thank you for coming to get me tonight. You may have saved Buster's life.'

She looked away, unable to meet his eyes. 'I'm glad.'

'Riding through a storm to get me was probably the most courageous act I've ever heard of,' he went on.

She glanced back at him, her eyes narrowing. 'Aren't you going to berate me for putting one of your valuable animals at risk?'

He smiled. 'Under the circumstances I hardly think so,' he said quietly. 'Even though it was a crazy thing to do.'

She swallowed hard, pinned like a butterfly by his mesmerising blue eyes.

'I didn't have any choice.'

He shook his head. 'That's not true. You could have chosen to stay in the house all evening and never ventured anywhere near the stables.' He looked at her thoughtfully. 'Why did you go, Kaylie?'

'Because I thought the horses might be afraid of the storm.' The simple explanation sounded ridiculous to her own ears, but he nodded.

'Even though you were afraid too.'

'Well, yes, but——'

'Then you had to make a second choice,' he continued as if she'd never spoken. 'You could quite justifiably have scuttled back to the warmth of the house, deciding it was none of your business. Instead, you went out into a storm to fetch help.' He took a step towards her and she hung her head, unable to meet the force of his probing eyes. 'By rights I should tan your hide.'

Startled, she glanced up, and her bones seemed to turn to jelly as she saw the look of tenderness on his face.

'Perhaps you haven't really changed so very much, Kaylie,' he murmured and she felt the warmth of his breath on her skin. 'Perhaps in some ways you are still the same sweet, head-strong, impetuous girl I once knew.'

He was going to kiss her—every fibre of her being knew it and longed for his caress, yet she couldn't bear it, couldn't cope with being in his arms, feeling his lips against her own, without caving in entirely and crying out her own love for him—a love so strong it must surely break through her own meagre defences of pride.

'You should get changed,' she said. 'Your evening suit will get ruined out here.'

A tiny, ironic smile played about his lips, but he nodded.

'True.' And before her astonished eyes he
began unbuttoning his starched white dress shirt.
Unthinkingly she backed off a couple of paces.

'I'll go and check on the other horses.'

'I've done that already,' he returned calmly.
'What's wrong, Kaylie? Scared of seeing me
without clothes? It never used to bother you when
we went skinny-dipping down at the river.
Remember?'

He shrugged the shirt off his broad shoulders
and, try as she might, she couldn't prevent her
eyes from feasting on the sight of his powerful
naked chest with its thick covering of silky black
hair, arrowing down to disappear beneath his
trousers. He hadn't had that in those far-off
skinny-dipping days. And though he'd always
had the build of an athlete, he hadn't had those
rippling muscles either.

'Remember, Kaylie?'

She dragged her reluctant eyes back to his face,
somehow managing to summon up enough co-
ordination to nod her head.

'Of course I remember. But that was a long
time ago. You've changed.' As soon as she'd said
the words she could have bitten her own tongue
out. So the sight of him was making her come
unglued—there was no need to let him know that.

He started to unbuckle the belt on his trousers,
then slid down the zip, and with a monumental
effort she broke through the hypnotic trance that
had been keeping her frozen in place, turning
away to find the bag of provisions she'd brought
from the house. Rummaging through it gave her
a good twenty seconds' grace, allowing some of

the heat to die from her cheeks. Her composure more or less regained, she turned back towards him, holding a thermos flask aloft.

'Coffee?' The word strangled in her throat as her eyes travelled slowly over the whole magnificent length of him. He'd shed everything but a pair of black briefs that clung lovingly to him, leaving nothing to the imagination.

'Flynn, please, you'll frighten the horses.' She tried for a light, frivolous laugh, then wished she hadn't bothered as it emerged distinctly ragged round the edges.

'I don't think so. Horses aren't particularly prudish in my experience.'

'I'm not prudish,' she retorted, stung by the implication. 'I just don't want you to catch your death of cold, that's all.'

'Then come over here and warm me up.'

The very idea jolted her so severely that she nearly dropped the flask.

'How about some coffee?' she suggested with more than a trace of desperation. 'That should do the trick.'

His eyes glinted challengingly. 'What's the matter, Kaylie? Scared?'

'Certainly not. It's just that—oh, Flynn, this is ridiculous.'

'There's nothing ridiculous about it. All I'm asking for is a little human warmth to thaw me out. Surely you wouldn't deny an old friend such a simple request?'

Torn in two by an aching longing to rush into his arms and an almost equally strong need for self-preservation, she gazed back at him helplessly.

'Come on,' he coaxed softly. 'I'm starting to shiver.'

Which was nothing to what he was making her do seconds later when she found herself nestled in his arms. She wasn't even sure how she'd got there, she realised dazedly, the feel of his chest beneath her cheek sending her temperature soaring. It was almost as if she'd been taken over by an outside force for the tiny space of time it had taken to cross the stable. No—not an outside force, but one from deep within, the one which could never hope to resist Flynn Donovan for long.

'You're freezing.' She stroked his back, loving the silken strength beneath her fingers. 'You must put some clothes on.'

'In a minute,' he murmured huskily. 'This is doing more to warm me than any clothes could.'

His hands slid down to cup her backside, pulling her closer still, and she couldn't stifle a groan as she felt him, hard and powerful against her.

'See what you do to me, Kaylie.' His words whispered through her hair, and she closed her eyes helplessly, torn apart by the rivers of longing coursing through her body. She couldn't let herself be fooled by his physical response to her— doubtless he'd felt this way countless times, perhaps with countless women. It was different for her—he was the only man who'd ever lit fires in her blood, the only one who ever could.

She raised her eyes to look at him, mustering her strength to put an end to this thing before the fires raged completely out of control, but even as the words formed on her lips he kissed them away and she was lost. The whole world seemed to spin away into oblivion as she stood, locked in his embrace. The only reality was there in the empty stable, the only truth in the touch of his fingers sliding beneath her clothes to stroke and caress her naked skin. All conscious thought fled, leaving her with only aching, hungry need.

She opened her mouth to him, thirsting for the taste and the feel of his probing, searching tongue, arching towards him as he slid her sweat-shirt upwards and bent his head to pay homage to her breasts, her nipples hardening beneath his lips. He rained a trail of kisses over her stomach, dropping to his knees before her as he undid the waistband of her jeans, and she drew in a sharp breath when his questing fingers slid unerringly downward to the very heart of her longing. She was boneless, mindless, liquid in his arms, no more able to resist than a moth could resist a flickering candle flame.

He swiftly stripped off the rest of her clothes, tossing them carelessly into the straw, then hooked one arm beneath her knees and lifted her effortlessly into his arms. She buried her face in his neck, breathing in the uniquely male fragrance of him, her tongue darting out to taste his skin.

'This is far from the setting I imagined for making love to you for the first time, Kaylie.' He set her gently down, quickly spreading the blanket over the thick bed of straw. 'But I doubt I could make it even two steps out of here.'

'You've thought about making love to me?' She was barely able to whisper the words.

He smiled. 'Probably every time I've ever made love.'

She closed her eyes, pierced by a sudden sweet, wild joy, yet lacerated at the same time by agonising jealousy.

'Don't tell me about other women,' she begged hoarsely. 'I can't stand the thought of anyone else in your arms.'

'Any more than I can bear to think of you with any of those damn city playboys,' he gritted out. 'I could tear them apart with my bare hands for daring to touch what is mine and mine alone.'

'But Flynn, I——'

'I don't want to hear,' he cut in harshly. 'But know this, Kaylie—I'm a jealous lover. Don't think you can lie with me now, and then return to any other men. I'd see them rot in hell before I'd let them touch you again.'

For answer she simply lay back against the blanket, pulling him down towards her. She'd never convince him with words that he was wrong, oh, so very wrong about those other imagined lovers in her life. But her body would tell him the truth, would show him in a way he could never doubt that she'd never lain with any other man. As his mouth claimed hers all over again she knew a second's hesitation. They were about to make love and neither was protected. Then the doubts took wing and flew—she'd dreamed of this moment for half of her lifetime; she couldn't let anything stand in her way now.

He moved on top of her and she welcomed his weight willingly, thrusting her fingers deep into his raven-black hair to bring him closer still. His mouth claimed hers and she whimpered as his hands stroked the satiny flesh between her thighs, teasing her to the point of madness.

'Sweet heaven, Flynn,' she whispered, 'I can't take much more of this. You're driving me crazy.'

He laughed exultantly, deep in his throat. 'I haven't even begun.'

Time lost its meaning as she found herself drowning once more in his kisses. Daylight could have come and gone a dozen times over and she'd never have known, every tiny shred of her consciousness centred on Flynn and the exquisite things he was making her feel. He was a superb lover—even though she had no way of comparing him to anyone else, still she knew instinctively that he was no newcomer to this game. It didn't matter—nothing mattered except that he was with her now, loving her with his body if not his mind. Now he'd always be a part of her and surely she'd always be a part of him, for surely no two people could come so close together and not leave a trace on the other?

Gently he nudged her knees apart and she moaned wildly with the touch of him against her. Slowly, oh, so slowly, he slid deep inside her and even as she felt a flash of pain she heard her own voice crying out his name as though her very soul was welcoming its mate. He seemed to hesitate, but her body closed around him, sheathing him in warm velvet, urging him on as he moved within her. She couldn't bear it—the beauty was too much, too intense, too incredible to endure even though she would have given everything just to hold on to one fleeting second of it. But she was out of control, no longer mistress of her own body. With a soft cry she felt herself go over the edge, just as a deep shudder shook his body and he groaned.

'Kaylie.'

'Hmm?' Through cloudy eyes she gazed up at him, still too dazed by the glory of it all to focus properly.

He stroked a wayward strand of hair back from her flushed cheek.

'We have to talk. I didn't know——'

Smiling she laid a finger on his lips, staying his words.

'Not now,' she said softly. 'Later.'

Let it be later, when reality returned, when they were both forced to face up to what had happened between them. Let the questions begin then, but not now, not now when she was filled with a sweet, glowing contentment and the arms of the man she loved were still wrapped about her, holding her close.

She slid one hand into his hair, pulling him towards her, putting her lips where her finger had been seconds before. Once she'd believed the spell he'd cast on her so many years before could only be broken by his making love to her. She'd been wrong. She could never have enough of this man—even now, as passion ebbed, the feel of his

mouth moving over hers was enough to send the
flames flickering into life all over again.

A silent voice echoed his name over and over
again like a litany in her brain and when he slid
down her body to tease her breasts with his
tongue she was powerless against a new hot flood
of longing. He moved lower still, his kisses
trailing over her stomach, sending an inferno
raging through her blood, and she whimpered,
completely at his mercy. He played her like a
master musician, bringing her again and again to
the very brink, but never allowing her to take the
headlong plunge till she felt she must surely
shatter in a million pieces.

At the very second when she knew she could
take no more he folded her in his arms just as a
sudden incredible onslaught of sensation shook
her to the very core of her being and she clung
to him as though he were a rock in a tempest-
lashed sea.

'Oh, Flynn,' she laughed shakily as the storm
slowly died away, leaving her spent and sated. 'I
never knew anything could be as glorious.'

'Hush, now.' He stroked her hair tenderly.
'Just rest. You've been through a lot today, little
one.'

Soothed by his gentle touch, she closed her
eyes, washed over by waves of warm and peaceful
contentment. Within seconds she'd drifted into
sleep, a beatific smile on her lips.

CHAPTER TEN

KAYLIE awoke to the sound of a loud and angry voice. Amanda's.

'Just what the hell is going on around here, Flynn? Why did you disappear so suddenly and without explanation from the ball last night? Have you any idea how foolish I felt having to make excuses for your absence when I didn't even know where you'd gone—or why?'

Bemused, Kaylie sat up, gazing in total confusion at the empty stable and at her own bed of straw. What was she doing here? And why was Amanda shouting at Flynn out in the yard? Heat suddenly flooded her cheeks as memory returned in a rush. So it hadn't been a dream—she really had lain in Flynn's arms all night long, really had made love with him. And it had been glorious—utterly, spellbindingly glorious. But now with the grey light of morning the glory had fled, leaving her alone, naked and horribly vulnerable with Amanda just a few feet away at the other side of the stable half-door.

Moving as quietly and stealthily as possible, she crawled round the floor, picking up her crumpled clothes, pulling them on as best she could. There seemed to be more straw clinging to her than was still lying on the floor, she realised. Amanda would doubtless guess at a glance just what had been going on. Still, with any luck, Flynn would draw her away, giving Kaylie a chance to escape.

'I came home because Buster was sick,' she heard Flynn say evenly. 'I've been here all night with him.'

'Buster? But how on earth . . . ?' Amanda's exclamation died abruptly as she walked towards the stable block and Kaylie's heart sank. She'd been seen.

'I see you had company during your long, lonely vigil.' The woman's voice dripped acid as she gazed with narrow, vindictive eyes at Kaylie. 'I'm so glad. I'd hate to think of you suffering such a trauma alone.'

Feeling for all the world like a schoolgirl caught out in a naughty prank, Kaylie finished pulling on her socks and boots, then walked out of the stable.

'Good morning, Amanda,' she said quietly. She couldn't bring herself to look at Flynn, too afraid of what she might see. Last night they'd been caught up in something too powerful to resist, but if she should see regret, or, worse still, contempt in his vivid blue eyes this morning she wouldn't be able to bear it.

'How nice of you to stand by Flynn in his time of trouble.' Amanda's mouth twisted malevolently. 'And how ironic, considering it was probably your fault that Buster had colic in the first place.'

'My fault?' Kaylie stared back at her, completely taken aback by the accusation. 'But I——'

'That's enough, Amanda,' Flynn cut in, but the blonde woman shook her head.

'It's far from enough. You just ask your precious Kaylie who fed Buster yesterday afternoon.'

Two sets of eyes bored into her, and to her horror Kaylie felt her cheeks begin to redden.

'Well, Kaylie?'

'I fed him.' Kaylie forced herself to speak calmly.

Flynn frowned. 'You fed him? But I categorically told you never to go near the feedstuffs again after the sugar-beet episode.'

'Laura asked her to do Buster's feed so she could get away early,' Amanda put in.

Kaylie was gripped by helpless frustration. It was bad enough that Amanda should lay the blame at her own door—now she was trying to implicate Laura too. But she was right—she had fed the horse on Laura's instructions.

She looked at Flynn and saw anger, cold and deadly, in his eyes, and something inside her seemed to die. He believed Amanda. Even after everything that had happened between them last night, even after holding her in his arms and loving her so tenderly, he believed Amanda. Pain sliced into her like a dagger. All she wanted was to fall to her knees and howl like a wounded animal. Only sheer dogged pride kept her on her feet.

'Laura's not to blame,' she said quietly. 'Whoever is responsible for Buster's illness, it's not her.'

'Go back to the house, Kaylie.' Flynn's voice was tight with barely controlled fury. 'I'll talk to you later.'

'Very well.' She gave a tiny nod. Then she walked away from him, keeping her head held high even as her world fell to ashes about her feet. Just as she reached the back door, she heard the sound of a car and turned to see Laura driving up.

'Morning!' Happily unaware of everything that had been happening, the young woman sent Kaylie a beaming grin. 'You can take that look off your face—your car's still in perfect working order, honest!'

Kaylie shook her head. 'It never occurred to me that it wouldn't be.'

'Then why so glum?'

Kaylie shrugged. 'Long story.' Realising she couldn't let Laura walk into a hornet's nest un-armed, she quickly explained the night's events, and the girl's expression went from incredulity to fury in seconds.

'They're blaming you?' she said, outraged. 'Don't worry—I'll tell Flynn the truth.'

Kaylie made a wearily dismissive gesture. 'Don't bother. It doesn't matter any more. Just make sure Flynn knows you had no part in it, that's all.'

Laura's eyes narrowed. 'Why? What are you going to do?'

'What I should have done days ago.' Kaylie smiled wryly. 'I'm going to leave.'

'No, Kaylie.'

'Yes, Laura.' She laid a hand on the other girl's shoulder. 'It's for the best. Flynn and I were friends long ago and I believed we could be again, but I was wrong. The longer I stay here, the further apart we become. I have to get away before we end up hating each other.' Not entirely true, she admitted silently. No matter what he did to her, she could never hate Flynn Donovan. 'Look, I want you to do a couple of things for me. Will you?'

'Of course I will, but——'

'Please, Laura—just accept that I know what I'm doing.' She took a deep, steadying breath. 'I want to get away as fast as possible, so could you send my things on for me? I'll write to you in a couple of days with my address.' She stared penetratingly into Laura's eyes. 'Do not, under any circumstances whatsoever, let Flynn have that address.' She gave a hollow little laugh. 'Not that he's likely to want it, but I'd rather just sever all ties now. Also, I want you to collect a film from the chemist shop in the village. I've left the ticket on the chest of drawers in my room. Give the photographs to Flynn.'

Laura shook her head wonderingly. 'Even after all this, you still want to help him?'

Kaylie grinned, with just a trace of the old impish sparkle in her grey eyes. 'Maybe it's really Buster I want to help. One way or another, that horse has been responsible for giving me some very memorable moments!' Impulsively she hugged the other girl. 'I hope we meet again—you've been a real friend.'

'It wasn't hard.' Laura's smile was wavery. 'Look after yourself, OK?'

'I will.' Suddenly in a hurry to be gone, Kaylie climbed into the driver's seat and switched on the ignition. Then with a final wave she drove out of the stable yard and along the farm drive to the main road. It was only when she'd passed safely through the village that she began to relax, but as she checked the rear-view mirror one more time she gave a wry little smile.

'Just what did you expect?' she muttered aloud to the empty car. 'Flynn to come chasing after you on a white charger, begging you to come home? Grow up, kid. This ain't the movies.'

And Flynn was no hero. That, perhaps, was the hardest truth of all.

She stopped off at the flat in Edinburgh only long enough to pick up some fresh clothes and fob off a desperately curious flatmate.

'You're only just back!' Beth wailed. 'Why are you going away again—and where? And why won't you tell me what's been happening?'

'I'm going away again because I need some time to myself,' Kaylie said calmly as she packed clean sweat-shirts into a case. 'I'm going to head south, and I won't tell you what's happening because I'm not ready to yet. OK?'

She could see from the way Beth's animated features were working that she was just about to explode with a veritable volley of questions, so she shut the suitcase firmly and headed towards the living-room, Beth hot on her heels.

'You'll have to be more precise about where you're going at least,' Beth pleaded. 'What if I need to get in touch urgently—if someone wants to commission work or something?'

Kaylie hesitated. Frankly it would suit her just fine to disappear right off the face of the earth, but her flatmate was right. It would be ridiculous to lose out on work just because she was hell-bent on doing a Greta Garbo act.

'OK,' she conceded. 'I'm going to the Lake District.'

Beth rolled her eyes heavenward. 'Give me a break! Finding a needle in a haystack I might just manage—but a photographer in the Lake District?'

Kaylie couldn't help but laugh at that. 'I'll phone you tonight when I know where I'm staying. Will that do?'

'I suppose it'll have to,' Beth returned morosely. 'But make sure you come back in a more talkative mood. It doesn't do anyone any good to bottle things up, you know.'

In theory she was right, Kaylie reflected as she headed the car southward. Only in this case pulling the stopper on the bottle might just have unleashed more than even Beth could handle. Since leaving Flynn's she'd been like some sort of automaton, going through all the actions of walking, talking and breathing without really registering a thing. It was almost as though someone had switched off her heart—or her emotions. It was early evening when she finally drew into a campsite car park. She'd deliberately headed off the beaten track, picking a site that scored high on privacy, even if its amenities left something to be desired. Here she could depend on having serious walkers and bird-watchers for neighbours, people too caught up in their own obsessions to worry unduly about hers.

By the time she'd set up camp and rustled up a meal she barely tasted she was bone-weary, exhausted by the strain of the day and the almost equal strain of trying to pretend none of it had happened. She dutifully phoned Beth, then crawled into her sleeping-bag, but as soon as she closed her tired eyes a picture of Flynn as she'd last seen him, tight-lipped and angry, flashed into her mind and she groaned heavily.

'Not now,' she moaned aloud. 'Leave me alone. Don't torture me this way.'

Her plea went unanswered. All through that long dark night she tossed and turned, unable to shut out the piercingly vivid pictures playing relentlessly in her mind. Just twenty-four hours earlier she'd been lying in his arms, holding him, loving him, touching the stars with him, and the agony of losing him so cruelly was like a bereavement. Maybe even worse, she reflected grimly, finally giving up the struggle to find sleep and switching on her torch to locate the coffee flask she'd filled before turning in. He'd been impressed that when faced with the choice between staying in a warm house and fetching help for Buster she'd opted for the latter even with all its dangers. But given a choice himself between believing Kaylie and believing Amanda, he hadn't hesitated for a second.

She was still awake when morning came and she welcomed its grey light like an old friend. At least now she could get up and do something, anything to keep occupied. It was the forced inactivity of the night that had proved her undoing. She wriggled out of the sleeping-bag, shivering a little in the cool morning air, then pulled on jeans and a warm sweater before sprinting across the campsite to the shower block.

'Today's a brand new day,' she informed her own reflection in a somewhat steamed-up mirror. 'And a brand new beginning. Today you're going to make a start on the rest of your life.'

Bolstered by her own pep talk, she even managed to whistle a perky little tune as she walked back across the site, smiling at other campers as they emerged sleepy-eyed and tousle-haired to face the day.

Back at the tent she pulled on her walking boots, picked up her camera gear, and headed for the hills, happy to become engrossed in photographing the many and varied wonders of the area's natural beauty. It had been good therapy, she reflected several hours later as she turned back for the campsite. Her heart might still be aching, but at least she'd lost that painfully bereft, disorientated feeling. Thanks to the camera, she knew now that she could survive without Flynn. Life would never be complete without him, but she could get by.

Then all of her new-found composure shattered in bits around her as she spotted Flynn sitting on the ground in front of her tent. For a second she wanted to flee, to run from the man who'd already wreaked such havoc in her life. Instead, she gritted her teeth and walked on, her heart thudding so loudly in her chest that she was sure he must be able to hear it too. He looked up with a smile as she approached and she had to swallow hard against a rush of joy she couldn't suppress.

'What are you doing here?'

'I could ask you the same thing,' he said softly and the Irish lilt in his voice wound round her heart like a blossoming flower. 'You're supposed to be at Cedar Wood Stables.'

She glowered down at him, forcing back the smile that was doing its best to break through.

'I never stay where I'm not wanted,' she said coolly. 'Well, not unless I have to,' she amended, remembering the reception she'd been given when she'd first arrived at the stables.

'Who said you weren't wanted?' The warmth in his blue eyes reached out to her, threatening to make a nonsense of all the resolutions she'd made to banish him from her mind. He reached up to take her hand in his and the touch of his fingers against her cool skin made her tremble.

'Would you like me to make a list?' She bit her lip, hating the quavery, uncertain note in her own voice. 'Laura and Mrs Mac were the only ones who even treated me as a human being. As far as the others were concerned, I was an undesirable alien species, or a particularly loathsome strain of the bubonic plague.'

'What about me?'

She closed her eyes, swaying slightly. How could she even begin to tell him how he'd made her feel?

'I'm sorry, Kaylie. I know I've given you a hard time. I was wrong.'

Her eyes snapped open. Flynn, apologising? More incredible still—Flynn admitting he'd been wrong? She shook her head, convinced her brains had become addled. She was dreaming; she had to be. Obviously realising he'd knocked her for six, Flynn grabbed his chance and gently tugged on the nerveless hand he still held captive, opening his arms to her as she tumbled to the ground, her legs unable to hold her up any longer.

'Did I hear correctly just now?' It was difficult to breathe with his face mere inches from her own, but, try as she might to make her legs stand up again, it seemed the message wasn't getting through from her brain.

'You did.'

'And when did you have this astounding revelation?' She'd never liked sarcasm, but right now it was the sole weapon left in the armoury.

'I've been coming to realise it for some time,' he said gravely. 'But I was too stubborn to accept I could have been wrong.'

'And pig-headed.'

He nodded solemnly, though there was more than a hint of laughter in his eyes. 'And pig-headed,' he agreed.

'And downright bloody-mindedly arrogant.'

'Kaylie!' His arms tightened about her, making her gasp. 'What do you want? Grovelling?'

She considered that for a second, then nodded. 'Possibly. But first I want to know what changed your mind. Was it the photographs?'

He stared at her quizzically. 'What photographs?'

'The ones I asked Laura to...' She broke off in mid-sentence, silenced by a ridiculous little surge of delight. He'd realised he was wrong even without the damning evidence of the film. He hadn't needed proof—he'd trusted her, even when there was no good reason to. Surely that must mean he felt something for her? But even as she began to melt inside, she very deliberately hardened her heart. After all he'd put her through, she wasn't about to let him off the hook that easily.

'Explain,' she demanded.

He stroked one hand over her hair, distracting her utterly, and she grabbed his fingers, holding them captive.

'The story starts a long time ago,' he said softly. 'When you started growing up.' He gave a wry little laugh. 'I couldn't cope with it, Kaylie— you'd always meant the world to me, tagging around behind me like a little puppy dog, but when I began to see the budding woman in you I knew I couldn't stick around to watch you grow.'

'Why not?' She could barely whisper the words.

'Because I'd have wanted to claim you for my own the very second you were old enough. And that wouldn't have been fair—you had to do your own growing.' He curved his fingers round her chin, forcing her to look at him. 'I'd been in love with you ever since the first day I saw you. I tried to tell myself it was something else, that you were just a kid, and that I was sorry for you. All the time we were at Emma's together, I tried to be the big brother you'd lost, but that grew more and more difficult as I watched you become ever more beautiful.'

She sent him a look of blank astonishment. 'Me? Beautiful? But that first day at the stables you said——'

'I know what I said,' he cut in. 'I was doing the only thing I could to stop myself from simply making you mine there and then. Heaven knows I wanted to.'

'What stopped you?'

'The same thing that made me disappear from Emma's home on your sixteenth birthday.' He gazed down at her, his eyes unreadable. 'Your legacy.'

'My legacy?' she frowned uncomprehendingly.

He nodded. 'Emma told me you were due to inherit your father's estate on your eighteenth birthday. She said he'd written a clause to that effect in his will, should anything happen to him.'

She shook her head impatiently. 'I know all that. But what does my father's will have to do with all of this?'

He smiled. 'Everything. Because it made you into an heiress, while I was a penniless nobody. I swore there and then that no one would ever call me a fortune hunter, just out for your money. So I left Emma's to seek my own fortune, intending to come back for you when I had some-

thing to offer.' His lips twisted self-deprecatingly.
'It took a while, but I was getting there, Kaylie—
sheer hard work and dogged persistence were
getting me there. And then . . .' He paused, his
eyes darkening in sudden anger.

'And then you had your accident,' she said
quietly.

He gave a single abrupt nod. 'And then I had
my accident.'

'What happened?' It pained her to ask,
knowing how much it must hurt him still to talk
about it, but she had to know, had to hear the
truth.

He shrugged. 'Nothing very dramatic. I was
jumping in a big competition abroad. Just as I
was approaching the last fence, my horse shied
at something—I'm not sure what, though I have
a vague memory of seeing something glinting.
Anyway, I rode him on, but we took off all
wrong, smashed into the fence, and he came
down on top of me. The horse got to his feet and
trotted off; I stayed down with a busted leg. The
rest you know.'

She nodded thoughtfully. 'Will your leg always
be bad?'

He toyed with a strand of her hair. 'There are
operations I could have. Somehow it didn't seem
worth while. None of the doctors could tell me
how it was likely to affect my riding—and until
your mad escapade on Mayfly I couldn't face
finding out the truth for myself, so I simply shut
that part of my life away.'

She absorbed that in silence for a long moment. 'Didn't Emma ever tell you the truth about my legacy?' she asked at last.

'I wouldn't allow her to talk about you at all,' he returned. 'I warned her that if she mentioned you in my presence I'd disappear out of her life as well.' He grinned with the memory. 'She gave me living hell of course, but she knew I meant it.'

Kaylie shook her head despairingly. 'I can barely believe this,' she said. 'My inheritance provided me with enough money to buy a flat in Edinburgh and to pay my own way through college. My father wasn't a rich man, Flynn. As for me, I lurch along between one assignment and the next, sometimes wondering where the next roll of film's coming from. Emma would have told you that if you'd only listened.'

His features seemed to tighten. 'Then how do you manage to afford your lifestyle?'

'My lifestyle?' She gave an exasperated little chuckle. 'Oh, Flynn, you have no idea of my lifestyle! I am not and never have been the socialite you seem determined to believe I am. I've worked extremely hard at my career, and I've accepted all sorts of assignments in all sorts of places.' She looked at him significantly. 'Including one which took me to an Edinburgh night-club on the same night that a society photographer was there taking shots for an article on the city jet-setters.' She paused, smiling a little as comprehension slowly dawned on his features. After a long moment he gave her a grin that could only be described as sheepish.

'You're telling me in a roundabout way that I've been an idiot?'

She nodded. 'On the button.'

He stared down at her for a long moment, then began to laugh.

'It's not funny!' she protested, though her own lips were twitching.

He shook his head. 'I'm laughing at the irony of it all. But who knows, maybe it's all been for the best. We were both too young to handle the kind of feelings we had for each other back then—we needed time apart to grow, to find out more about ourselves.

And what have we found out, Flynn? How do we feel about each other now? The questions danced in her brain, but she bit her lips, refusing to voice them. Now that the barriers were down, it was obvious he still felt all the old youthful fondness for her, but he hadn't spoken a single word of love. Perhaps fondness was all he had left, and she wasn't about to reveal the depth of her feelings.

Suddenly she tensed, as an errant thought crystallised in her mind.

'That glint,' she said sharply. 'The one that made your horse shy. What could have caused it?'

He gave her a look of mild amusement. 'Kaylie, I barely remember now.'

'I think you remember very well,' she said firmly. 'What could have caused it, Flynn?'

He shrugged. 'A bit of silver paper catching the sun, perhaps; who knows?'

'Or a mirror held up deliberately to catch the horse's eye.'

She could tell from the look on his face that the suggestion didn't shock him.

'What makes you say that?' he said with a nonchalance that didn't quite ring true.

'Is it possible, Flynn?' She twisted round to gaze urgently into his eyes. 'Could someone have engineered the accident? Did anyone dislike you that much?'

For a long moment she thought he would refuse to answer, then he gave a single reluctant nod.

'I discovered one of my rivals was using dirty tricks in training horses,' he said.

'Like rapping?'

He looked at her in surprise. 'How on earth do you know about rapping?'

'Never mind that now. Go on.'

'Well, yes, he was rapping his animals, but a lot more besides.' His features darkened angrily. 'Those methods make me sick—either a horse is talented and can do the job, or it can't. It should never be bullied and tortured.'

'What did you do?'

'Nothing.' He rubbed one hand wearily over his face. 'I tackled him about it, of course—we had quite a show-down in fact. And I threatened to report him to the appropriate equestrian authorities. But the very next day, I was flat on my back in a hospital ward.'

'Is he still training horses?' Kaylie asked.

'No, thank God. He got out of the game shortly afterwards.'

'Flynn,' Kaylie said slowly, 'does Amanda know about any of this?'

He nodded. 'She should. The man I've been talking about is her brother.'

If she hadn't been sitting on the ground, Kaylie would probably have keeled right over, knocked sideways by this totally unexpected news.

'Her brother?' she echoed disbelievingly.

'After the accident she came to me—told me she knew what her brother had been up to, and said she was deeply ashamed. She offered to run the yard till I was back on my feet—then we became partners.'

Kaylie closed her eyes, trying to take all of it in. Then she took a deep, shuddering breath. 'I don't know how to tell you this,' she said in a voice that was low and full of anguish. 'You probably won't even believe me, but I swear I've got proof to back up what I'm about to tell you.' She paused, gazing sightlessly at her own fingers. 'Amanda's been rapping your horses.' She waited for the explosion, her whole body tensing.

'I know,' Flynn said calmly.

Her head shot up. 'You know?'

He nodded. 'I've been suspecting as much for some time, but I haven't been able to prove anything.' His lips thinned. 'For a long time I think I was blind—I kept blaming myself every time something in the yard went wrong. It was only when you arrived that I became sure there was foul play going on.'

'When I arrived? Why?'

'Because you landed in hot water more often than any normal person could possibly manage.'

He grinned teasingly. 'I knew all of the things that happened couldn't really have been your fault, but quite frankly I didn't do anything about it because I believed it would be all to the good if you grew so sick of the place that you decided to leave. Having you around was doing me no good at all.'

'Thanks,' she said, offended.

He laughed, dropping a light kiss on to her hair. 'Don't go all sulky on me. You have to understand—I thought I was dealing with a city playgirl, and it was tearing me in two to think you could have changed so much from the girl I'd once loved.'

His last casual words sliced into her like sharp knives, but she managed with an effort to keep her features expressionless. Well, at least she now knew the truth—she'd had it from his own lips. She was the girl he had 'once loved'. Had she really expected anything else?

'Amanda finally dropped herself in it when she blamed you for Buster's colic.' His lips tightened. 'I hadn't said anything about colic, so there was no way she could have known about it—unless she'd had some hand in it.'

'Is Amanda still at the stables now?' She shot him a look of pure alarm. 'You can't have left her there alone, surely—she could be doing anything——'

'Hush, hush!' He laid a finger on her lips. 'Amanda and Claire were both given their marching orders yesterday—as you'd have found out for yourself if you'd stuck around long enough.' He frowned with the memory. 'Before they left I insisted they spill the beans—apparently Amanda had been very bitter about what happened to her brother. She blamed me for his leaving the horse world. And she'd sworn to somehow discredit me in the world's eyes.'

'So at some stage she'd have revealed that your horses were being rapped?'

He nodded grimly. 'That was the plan. And she'd probably have succeeded, too—if not for you.' The grimness faded from his features as he gazed down at her. 'When I asked you to go back to the house yesterday, it was because I didn't particularly want you to witness the kind of anger I can be capable of, but you went rushing off half-cocked, leaving me with a Sherlock Holmes job on my hands finding you again.'

'How did you find me?' Unconsciously she nestled back against his powerful frame and his arms tightened about her.

'By persuading our esteemed solicitor friend to part with your Edinburgh address—and then turning the full force of my charm on to your flatmate.'

Kaylie groaned. 'I bet she was a total pushover!'

He laughed. 'Correct. But I had to swear I'd return and tell her exactly what happened.' He slid her a teasing sideways look. 'She also made me promise she could be your chief bridesmaid at our wedding.'

'She what?' Shocked beyond measure, Kaylie tried to pull away, but Flynn's arms held her captive. 'I'm sorry, Flynn, that girl sometimes suffers from a major mouth problem. But I don't know what could have put such a ridiculous idea into her head.'

'I did,' he returned calmly.

'You did?' For a moment she seriously wondered if she was losing her mind. 'How?'

'By telling her we'd be getting married at the earliest possible opportunity. It's true, isn't it?' The blue eyes gazed into her own. 'It's always been true, Kaylie. You and I were meant for each other from the very first day we met.'

She slumped back against him, all the breath knocked out of her.

'Don't you think you could at least have asked me?' she said weakly.

'I'm asking you now,' he said gravely. 'I love you more than life itself, Kaylie. Will you marry me?'

Hardly able to bear the sweetness of the moment she buried her face in his shoulder, breathing in the faint aroma of horses from his tweed jacket.

'Yes,' she murmured breathlessly. 'Oh, yes.'

He tilted her chin upwards with one gentle hand, his mouth finding hers in a kiss that sealed their love forever. Then Kaylie gave a soft little laugh.

'The ridiculous thing about all of this is that we still don't even know what Emma bequeathed to us in her legacy.'

Flynn smiled. 'I think we've already got everything she wanted us to have,' he said tenderly. 'She couldn't have left us anything more precious than love.'

4 FREE

Romances and 2 FREE gifts just for you!

You can enjoy all the
heartwarming emotion of true love for FREE!
Discover the heartbreak and happiness,
the emotion and the tenderness of the modern
relationships in Mills & Boon Romances.

We'll send you 4 Romances as a special offer
from Mills & Boon Reader Service,
along with the opportunity to have 6 captivating
new Romances delivered to your door each month.

Claim your FREE books and gifts overleaf...

An irresistible offer from Mills & Boon

Become a regular reader of Romances with Mills & Boon Reader Service and we'll welcome you with 4 books, a CUDDLY TEDDY and a special MYSTERY GIFT all absolutely FREE.

And then look forward to receiving 6 brand new Romances each month, delivered to your door hot off the presses, postage and packing FREE! Plus our free Newsletter featuring author news, competitions, special offers and much more.

This invitation comes with no strings attached. You may cancel or suspend your subscription at any time, and still keep your free books and gifts.

It's so easy. Send no money now. Simply fill in the coupon below and post it to -
Reader Service, FREEPOST, PO Box 236, Croydon, Surrey CR9 9EL.

NO STAMP REQUIRED

Free Books Coupon

Yes! Please rush me 4 FREE Romances and 2 FREE gifts! Please also reserve me a Reader Service subscription. If I decide to subscribe I can look forward to receiving 6 brand new Romances for just £10.80 each month, postage and packing FREE! If I decide not to subscribe I shall write to you within 10 days - I can keep the free books and gifts whatever I choose. I may cancel or suspend my subscription at any time. I am over 18 years of age.

Ms/Mrs/Miss/Mr _____ EP56R

Address _____

_____

Postcode _____ Signature _____

Forthcoming Titles

DUET
Available in June

The Carole Mortimer Duet **VELVET PROMISE**
TANGLED HEARTS

The Sally Wentworth Duet **MISTAKEN WEDDING**
SATAN'S ISLAND

BEST SELLER ROMANCE
Available in July

THE COURSE OF TRUE LOVE Betty Neels
STORM CLOUD MARRIAGE Roberta Leigh

MEDICAL ROMANCE
Available in July

JUST WHAT THE DOCTOR ORDERED Caroline Anderson
LABOUR OF LOVE Janet Ferguson
THE FAITHFUL TYPE Elizabeth Harrison
A CERTAIN HUNGER Stella Whitelaw

Available from W.H. Smith, John Menzies, Martins, Forbuoys,
most supermarkets and other paperback stockists.

Also available from Mills & Boon Reader Service,
Freepost, P.O. Box 236, Thornton Road, Croydon,
Surrey CR9 9EL.

Readers in South Africa - write to:
Book Services International Ltd, P.O. Box 41654,
Craighall, Transvaal 2024.

Next Month's Romances

Each month you can choose from a wide variety of romance with Mills & Boon. Below are the new titles to look out for next month, why not ask either Mills & Boon Reader Service or your Newsagent to reserve you a copy of the titles you want to buy — just tick the titles you would like and either post to Reader Service or take it to any Newsagent and ask them to order your books.

Please save me the following titles:	Please tick	√
THE SEDUCTION OF KEIRA	Emma Darcy	
THREAT FROM THE PAST	Diana Hamilton	
DREAMING	Charlotte Lamb	
MIRRORS OF THE SEA	Sally Wentworth	
LAWFUL POSSESSION	Catherine George	
DESIGNED TO ANNOY	Elizabeth Oldfield	
A WOMAN ACCUSED	Sandra Marton	
A LOVE LIKE THAT	Natalie Fox	
LOVE'S DARK SHADOW	Grace Green	
THE WILLING CAPTIVE	Lee Stafford	
MAN OF THE MOUNTAINS	Kay Gregory	
LOVERS' MOON	Valerie Parv	
CRUEL ANGEL	Sharon Kendrick	
LITTLE WHITE LIES	Marjorie Lewty	
PROMISE ME LOVE	Jennifer Taylor	
LOVE'S FANTASY	Barbara McMahon	

If you would like to order these books in addition to your regular subscription from Mills & Boon Reader Service please send £1.80 per title to: Mills & Boon Reader Service, Freepost, P.O. Box 236, Croydon, Surrey, CR9 9EL, quote your Subscriber No:.................................... (If applicable) and complete the name and address details below. Alternatively, these books are available from many local Newsagents including W.H.Smith, J.Menzies, Martins and other paperback stockists from 9th July 1993.

Name:..

Address:..

....Post Code:...........................

To Retailer: If you would like to stock M&B books please contact your regular book/magazine wholesaler for details.

You may be mailed with offers from other reputable companies as a result of this application. If you would rather not take advantage of these opportunities please tick box ☐